MW00629353

Considering
Holotropic Breathwork

Essays and Articles on the Sociological, Therapeutic, and Spiritual
Functions and Effects of the Grof Breathwork

Kylea Taylor

Hanford Mead Publishers, Inc.
Santa Cruz, California USA

Considering
Holotropic Breathwork

Kylea Taylor

Email: info@hanfordmead.com
Website: www.hanfordmead.com

FIRST EDITION

ISBN 13: 978-1-59275-007-8 (alk. paper)

ISBN 10: 1-59275-007-9 (alk. paper)

Manufactured in the United States of America

This edition is printed on Ph neutral paper that meets the American National Standards Institute Z39.48 Standard.

10 9 8 7 6 5 4 3 2 1

Library of Congress Cataloging-in-Publication Data

Taylor, Kylea.
 Considering holotropic breathwork : essays on the sociological, therapeutic, and spiritual functions and effects of the Grof breathwork / Kylea Taylor.
     p. cm.
 Includes bibliographical references and index.
 ISBN 978-1-59275-007-8 (alk. paper)
 1. Holotropic breathwork. I. Title.

RZ403.H65T39 2007
615.5'3—dc22

                                        2007045434

Contents

Acknowledgments

These essays and articles have been written during the sixteen years between 1991 to 2007. They present some of my thinking about the functions and effects of Holotropic Breathwork, and reflect my own interests in addiction and trauma recovery, spiritual emergency, kundalini, and SoulCollage®. I am grateful to all who have contributed to my experiences in and my thinking about Holotropic Breathwork. I especially thank Stanislav and Christina Grof, Jim Schofield, Tav and Cary Sparks and my colleague Diane Haug. I acknowledge the crucial support of Rick Doblin, Holger Dumstrei, Karen Paine-Gernee, and my other 1984 Esalen monthlong friends and my Grof Transpersonal Training "Group A" and our counterparts in "Group B," and I honor and thank all those I have worked with in Holotropic Breathwork sessions.

I know that this deceptively simple technique developed by the Grofs is really quite amazing and life-changing. I know this from breathing on the mat myself, from facilitating Breathwork as a sitter and as a facilitator, by working with breathers as a therapist for post-breathwork integration, and through discussions with colleagues who report similar effects. I have been privileged indeed to be along on this journey.

~1~

A Description of
Holotropic Breathwork

[Published first in Allison, N. [Ed.] (1999.) The Illustrated Encyclopedia of Body-Mind Disciplines, *revised 2005.]*

Definition

Holotropic Breathwork is a method of self-exploration that combines rapid, deep breathing, evocative music, and focused bodywork. The term *holotropic* is derived from Greek roots, *holos*, meaning "whole" and *trepin*, meaning "to move in the direction of." The two together give the meaning *moving toward wholeness.* Plants turn in the direction of the sun in heliotropic motion. In the same way, during a holotropic session, the human organism moves to integrate, to make itself whole, and to heal the various injured or fragmented parts of the self. Holotropic Breathwork assists this process by inducing a state of non-ordinary consciousness and by creating a safe context within which to reconnect with self, others, and spirit.

Holotropic Breathwork aims to bring the mind and body together in a non-ordinary state of consciousness, which provides more conscious access to buried memories and aspects that may be hidden under ordinary conditions. While Holotropic Breathwork can be effective as part of the treatment for mental and physical disorders, it is more often approached as a shamanic activity for the recovery of the deep past and entry into the spiritual realm.

Many experiences arise in the process of this work, but having Breathwork experiences *per se*, (or any particular experience, such as rebirth or ecstasy) is not the purpose. The goals are wholeness, healing, and wisdom. Experiences are the means to these goals. When the body and mind enter a state of non-ordinary consciousness through controlled breathing, the inner wisdom uses the opportunity to work toward physical, mental, emotional, and spiritual healing, and developmental change. Holotropic Breathwork operates under the principle that we are our own best healers.

Holotropic Breathwork incorporates controlled breathing, music, one-on-one supervision, art, a flexible and open-ended time period, and thorough training of its practitioners—all of which elements promote safety and healing in non-ordinary states of consciousness.

Participants in Holotropic Breathwork may see emotionally charged visual images, sense energy moving through their bodies, receive intuitive insights, and clarify troublesome issues in their lives. Often participants report that they relieve accumulated stress, release emotions from old traumas, gain an increased trust in themselves and their bodies, and feel that they have understood and can now transcend old patterns of behavior that have brought unwanted results.

The history of Holotropic Breathwork

Stanislav Grof, M.D., a Czech psychiatrist trained in Prague during the 1950s, and his wife, Christina Grof, developed this powerful and natural technique from modern consciousness research and their study of ancient spiritual systems. A study of Jung's theories of the collective unconscious and his own personal experiences convinced Grof that faith in reason had led modern science to espouse a mechanistic model of the mind, incapable of assessing or utilizing its true range of powers. He was particularly interested in determining the scope and nature of experiences generally relegated to the category of parapsychological phenomena.

A breakthrough in the manufacture of psychedelic drugs gave Grof a way to experiment with altered states of consciousness in treating patients. He also took psychedelics himself and realized that there were broad similarities between certain drug-induced states of mind and the experiences attained through meditative, mystic, and shamanic activities.

After emigrating to the United States, Grof continued his research into non-ordinary consciousness and parapsychology at the Maryland Psychiatric Research Center, Johns Hopkins University, and eventually at the Esalen Institute in Big Sur, California.

The Grofs began facilitating workshops in 1976. They offered their first structured training programs in 1987. Together they facilitated Holotropic Breathwork sessions for more than 25,000 people from 1987-1994. Stanislav Grof's many books, including *Realms of the Human Unconscious* (1975), *Beyond the Brain* (1985), *Psychology of the Future* (2002), and *The Ultimate Journey* (2006) have contributed to the steady rise of interest in the Holotropic Breathwork technique and transpersonal psychology.

The Holotropic Breathwork experience

Holotropic Breathwork is presented by facilitators certified by the Grof Transpersonal Training. Before the first breathing experience, Holotropic Breathwork participants receive an in-depth theoretical preparation that includes a description of the major types of phenomena that occur in holotropic sessions (biographical, perinatal, and transpersonal) and technical instructions for working together in pairs as breather and sitter. Physical and emotional contraindications are discussed, and if there are any concerns, expert assessment is obtained. A medical history of difficulty with cardiovascular function, a diagnosis of glaucoma, or severe emotional disorder are all examples of conditions which preclude participation in public sessions of Holotropic Breathwork.

The Holotropic Breathwork experience is mostly internal and largely nonverbal, without interventions. Participants work in pairs, alternating the roles of breather and sitter. As sitters, they sit beside and watch over their companions, providing a sense of shelter and support and attending to any needs they may have. As breathers, they lie down on mats on the floor. The facilitators lead a guided relaxation to help the breathers relax their bodies in preparation for the breathing. At the end of the relaxation, the facilitators instruct the breathers to breathe deeper and faster than usual. The facilitators begin to play evocative or rhythmic music as the breathing deepens. The music continues for three hours. As the breathing continues, the breathers enter states of non-ordinary consciousness.

What is visible from the outside varies. Many people are perfectly still, as they would be in deep meditation. Some begin rocking or making other rhythmic movement. Some cry out, moan, weep, or express anger. Sometimes the breather asks for help in expressing feelings or sensations. The experiences vary from individual to individual and from session to session. The same individual will often have different experiences each time he or she does Breathwork.

The average Holotropic Breathwork session lasts between two and three hours. At the end of the session, when the facilitator checks in with the breather, the facilitator may offer a special form of bodywork, called focused energy release work, if the breathing has not resolved all of the emotional and physical tensions activated during the sessions. The basic principle of this work is to take clues from the breather, whose inner healer has brought up certain material because of the permission of the breath and the setting, and to create a situation in which the existing symptoms are amplified. While the energy and awareness are held in this part of the body, the subject is encouraged to express fully his or her response to the energy in a way that feels congruent with and matches the intensity that the breather is feeling. This form of focused energy release work is an essential part of the Holotropic approach and plays an important role in the completion and integration of the experience.

Participants in Holotropic Breathwork report often that they receive intuitive insights and clarify troublesome areas of their lives. They also report that the technique promotes self-healing through the release of accumulated stress and trauma and a sense of greater connection with physical, emotional, and spiritual parts of oneself.

The Grof Transpersonal Training

Certification in the Grof Transpersonal Training requires about 600 hours of training and at least two years to complete. This allows time for integration of the life-changing material that inevitably arises when people do Breathwork over an extended period. The experiential part of the training builds a deep trust in one's own inner wisdom. By embarking on and completing many journeys of their own, trainees gain the conviction that they can truly trust the internal guidance and process of each participant. This allows facilitators to convey their intrinsic faith in the process to any participant who may become frightened at some part of the inner journey.

The Grof Transpersonal Training, ably managed by Tav and Cary Sparks for many years, includes instruction related to the major components of the technique: breathing, music, art, and focused energy release work. It also provides a broad range of information on many issues that can arise as part of the work. Some of the subjects covered include: abnormal psychology, pharmacology, childhood sexual abuse, drug and alcohol abuse, world cosmologies, theologies, shamanism, new theories of physics and other sciences, astrology, alchemy, imagery in non-ordinary states of consciousness, perinatal and transpersonal themes in art and culture, the psychological and philosophical meaning of death, psychic phenomena, the use of intuition in transpersonal work, meditation, unusual transpersonal experiences, and ethical issues relevant to working with those in non-ordinary states.

The Grofs have trademarked the name Holotropic Breathwork to ensure that deep experiential work conducted under this name is only done with the thorough training and experience provided by the Grof Transpersonal Training.

~2~

The Practice of Sitting in Holotropic Breathwork

What One Learns about Oneself and Relationship while Being with a Breather

[First published in 2001 in The Healing Breath, *an online journal and revised 2005.]*

> *My first breathing experience was not [just] memorable. My first sitting was unforgettable.*[1]
>
> ~Jack Silver

Jack Silver, a certified Holotropic Breathwork practitioner, wrote of his heart-opening experience while *sitting* for the first time for his wife in a workshop with 100 participants. In the sitting experience, he felt he was sitting for all in the room, for all in the world. He goes on to say that sitting, rather than *breathing*, might well be the real spiritual practice of Holotropic Breathwork:

> *Later, I mused that the real teaching was the sitting, the breathing only a means of distracting our attention away from attainment-oriented practices, while the affect of directed attention, compassion-in-action, and*

15

opening of the heart occurred and became manifest. So strong was my first sitting experience.[2]

I, too, have felt for a long time that sitting is as at least as important a component in the Holotropic Breathwork experience as the breathing. They are complementary of course. The sitting role requires a breather. Likewise, the breathing experience is greatly enhanced by the practice of having a peer sitter for each breather. Silver writes, "For me, the Breathwork has two practices, two teachings."[3] Those two practices, sitting and breathing, exist within a ritual structure that underlies and supports Holotropic Breathwork—its principles, its theories, and its practice.

Sitting is part of the ritual setting for Holotropic Breathwork

Holotropic Breathwork is a technique, but it is better described as a ritual[4] structure that provides a safe *set and setting* — a container for whatever wants to happen when participants are breathing into a holotropic or non-ordinary state of consciousness. Stanislav Grof has said that, because someone in a non-ordinary state of consciousness has extraordinary sensitivity to external factors, it is vital that the experiencer have an understanding of the purpose and general approach of the technique (set), and that he or she know what the physical and interpersonal elements of the situation (setting) will be.[5] All the components of Holotropic Breathwork work together to provide a theoretical set and setting that can contain most deep processes. Both set and setting provide the "protection, permission, and connection" that inspire participants to trust and go as deeply as possible in each Breathwork experience.

Stephen Gilligan, a teacher of Eriksonian hypnosis and a psychological theorist who developed the therapeutic model called Self-Relations, describes the characteristics of ritual,[6] which include, "...a predetermined behavioral sequence....special symbols mark ritual space....pre- and post-phases are used as inductions into and exits out of ritual space. And binding commitments are secured to promote involvement and heighten the drama and significance of the event."[7] All these elements are included in the structure of a Holotropic Breathwork workshop. [See also Chapter 8 of this book.]

The sitter/breather dyad in Holotropic Breathwork

Holotropic Breathwork is most often done in a group setting and includes two Breathwork sessions. Participants work in partnership, so that one partner is the breather and the other is the sitter for one session. In the second session there is reciprocity; the roles reverse. Thus, there is one-on-one supervision of the one who is breathing at all times.[8] There is also overall facilitation by certified Holotropic Breathwork facilitators, but the one-on-one attention by a peer, provided by the sitter function, is a very important component of the work. The partners agree to serve each other in this time-limited and context-limited way. This agreement is one of the "binding commitments...secured to promote involvement and heighten the drama and significance of the event."[9]

How sitting came to be part of Holotropic Breathwork

The sitter/breather dyad was added to the Holotropic Breathwork technique quite organically and spontaneously. Stanislav and Christina Grof had been facilitating groups of breathers and experimenting with various ways of structuring group work at Esalen Institute in Big Sur, California. One day, Stan had a sudden back injury that prevented his doing direct work with the participants. With necessity as the mother of invention, the Grofs decided to ask the participants to choose partners and to facilitate *two* sessions of Breathwork so that the partners could reciprocate in attending to each other. The design worked so well and was so appreciated by the participants that the breather/sitter dyad was incorporated into the Grof model of Breathwork.

Gifts from the sitter to the breather

Learning from the role of sitter

One-on-one attention—the practical aspects

In Holotropic Breathwork there is implicit permission to access deep, unknown places. *Protection* must be commensurate with *permission.* The balance of both creates safe set and setting that allows one to go beyond the place where he or she knows the way. The sitter's duty is to take care of ordinary reality, so the breather can let go of having to monitor the environment and can feel free and safe to go as far into the inner world (non-ordinary reality) as possible. The sitter fetches a drink of water, supports the breather on a walk to the bathroom, covers up the breather if the breather is cold, holds a hand, and reminds the breather to continue breathing if the breather wants that kind of assistance.

The sitter also protects the breather from intrusion (*e.g.,* by others or environment) and from self-harm or from harming others (*e.g.,* by bumping into the wall or other breathers.)

The relationship between someone in a non-ordinary state of consciousness (breather) and someone who remains grounded in ordinary consciousness (sitter) is a sacred and delicate one. It requires a reaching of consciousness on the part of the sitter, an attention to nuance, and a meditation on the chasm between the two states and the bridge that can be built to join them. The value of the sitter is not just in his or her ability to one-sidedly see, hear, or touch. The healing of the original wound (*e.g.,* omission of nurture or abuse in childhood) cannot take place outside of relationship, because it was the very lack of relationship that *is* the wound.

The gift of the sitter is that the sitter responds *in relationship*. The relationship is the two-way flow of seeing and being seen, hearing and being heard, touching and feeling. Relationship, the essence of the sacred web of all life, is present and is available to be experienced and acknowledged in the Holotropic Breathwork workshop in the form of the sitter/breather relationship.[10]

Witnessing in Breathwork

A sitter is certainly more than a tool for a breather to get plenty of tissues or to get that extra blanket adjusted more quickly. Being a sitter can also be infinitely more than just a role one must tolerate and trade in order to breathe in the *other* session of a Holotropic Breathwork workshop.[11]

I remember Stan Grof talking about Ashley Montagu's thesis[12] that a newborn baby needs the experience of being seen, heard, and touched. I think many of us have been wounded by an early experience of not being seen, heard, or touched. The sitter/breather relationship can begin to heal that wound.[13]

Tenderness, both emotional and physical, is a major part of corrective experience in a Holotropic Breathwork session. When breathers are reliving birth, or early childhood, they often feel the trauma of omission. They did not get the sponsoring they needed at those early times. The regression allows, to some degree, a corrective experience of being well-nurtured and re-parented. Because of the group context, there is a feeling of safety in receiving physical touch that would be difficult to achieve in a one-on-one therapy session. People have had significant realignments in self-concept from such nurturing contact, feeling at long last, *I am touchable, I am wanted, I am seen,* and *it is okay to be here (to be born, to be alive).* Compassionate witnessing can also balance the experience of reliving trauma. A kind witness who sees and is empathic, and who is willing to feel into the pain the breather is experiencing, can make the experience tolerable.[14]

A sitter who is a crucial part of such corrective healing usually feels a deep satisfaction from his or her ability to give such a gift and make such a connection to the breather.

In Holotropic Breathwork the holotropic state often spontaneously includes a kind of bi-modal consciousness. This is to say that at the same time one is deeply inside the experience, one also usually has a witness self present to view what is happening with a more objective perspective, to sponsor the reliving of trauma, a feeling of cosmic unity, or other experience. The breather's sitter, witnessing the breather's experience, also sponsors the breather's inner witness self by modeling (being an outer representation of) the witness function or role.[15] Having a witness heightens the breather's awareness so that the witness part of the breather is awakened even while the breather is fully engaged in, for example, the reliving of a perinatal experience.

Learning 'non-doing' as a 'helper' in Breathwork and in ordinary life

In Holotropic Breathwork, the holotropic or non-ordinary state activates the inner healer so that it can show both breather and sitter the trajectory of the healing energy. In interacting with the spontaneous healing energy, the breather, the sitter, and the facilitators refrain from such interference as anticipating, directing, or enabling the unfolding process. The act of supporting or midwifing the energy without getting in its way is called 'non-doing'.[16] Neither sitter nor breather has to know where the energy is going, or what will be the outcome. They need only cooperate with the inner healer as it reveals itself moment by moment. Activated by Breathwork, the inner healer (or inner wisdom, higher power, Spirit) moves through the inner, huge, dark warehouse of the psyche, shining a light. The light finally focuses on and brightens some neglected corner from where is found the perfect piece of not-yet integrated material. This material seems to be selected when it is ready to come forward into consciousness. Our job as sitter for the breather is to trust the inner healer's choice of material and method, to witness what is coming forward and, as appropriate, to encourage expression and integration of the material.[17] As sitters we also have the opportunity to learn a great deal about ourselves.

Widening the focus of awareness

Sitting is a type of meditation. It is similar to vipassana[18] meditation. In Holotropic Breathwork, a sitter sometimes focuses in a one-pointed way on the breather, and sometimes has a multi-focused consciousness. In the latter case, the sitter is practicing (usually without consciously doing so) holding simultaneously an awareness of both the breather's process and needs and all the inner emotions, motivations, and thoughts that are moving through himself or herself. This wider focus of awareness may also at times expand beyond the breather/sitter dyad to the container that holds them both. That container includes the Holotropic Breathwork techniques and theory, the facilitators, the other sitter/breather dyads in the room, and the field of energy that is being created in the room at that moment.

This practice of widening consciousness is another way in which sitting makes new skills available to ordinary life. I remember a time when a television camera crew, with the permission of the participants, came to film a Holotropic Breathwork group session which Stan and Christina Grof was facilitating. The crew had a great deal of technical skill and much experience in aiming cameras at many kinds of subjects, but the men did not seem to be experienced at being in the midst of a group of people who were all in deep emotional process. From the blank, dissociated looks on the crew's faces, and based on the many times I saw each of them with a camera hanging unused at their sides, looking amazed at one of the breathers' emotional expressions, I imagined that their own emotions and memories were being triggered by the folks lying on their mats on the floor. I think, because of the TV crew members' lack of practice with simultaneous holding their technical skills, their own emotions, and a compassionate attention to others, that they were overwhelmed and needed to dissociate as best they could from what was happening.

As sitters and facilitators we all have these moments of dissociation when attention strays or disappears, but with the continuing practice of sitting for breathers in Holotropic Breathwork sessions, we are gradually able to hold more of ourselves, more of the other, and more of the environment in our conscious awareness simultaneously.

Sitting—An opportunity to develop and balance ourselves

Observing our own fears, desires, and distractions

The fears and desires that usually manage our lives unconsciously arise in meditation practice and are also quite likely to arise while sitting. I have heard it said that relationship is the best guru. Sitting, as meditation, provides us with a setting where we are less distracted from our unconscious motivations. It also puts the focus on our present moment of relationship with our breather and with any of our judgments about participants or other elements of the workshop. Sitters have reported epiphanies realizing their judgments about their breather or nearby sitters had been recreations of patterns in relationship throughout their lives. They have, in the sitter role, the opportunity to reclaim and understand projections they have unconsciously been putting upon others.[19]

Sitting enables us to become more aware of our own emotions and motivations. This often has a balancing effect on our personalities. In the sitter role, as well as in the breather role, we move *holotropically,[20] towards wholeness.* We become more conscious of our own inner dynamics so that, instead of reacting to situations with a limited and pre-programmed repertoire, we can respond flexibly and appropriately to a variety of situations, drawing upon a greater range of inner resources.

Although people are complex and don't necessarily fit neatly into categories such as those listed below, we usually can recognize those tendencies and strengths we have already, as well as those we need to develop.

Balancing a tendency in life to over-emote

For people who easily express emotions, sitting is a balancing time in which they practice knowing, naming, feeling, but then, instead of expressing (which is the role of the breather), they have the opportunity to practice another skill—one of letting the emotional energy move through without acting on it. This can be particularly helpful in strengthening one's 'inner sitter'. They can learn skills that will enable them to sit more calmly with their own emotional parts, so that they are not as dependent on others to play the calm and analytical roles in their lives.

People who have most often been in the 'patient' or 'client' roles may feel they are often in the *receiver* role with others, but that they don't have much to give others. These sitters can be pleasantly surprised to learn how much they really can offer to their breathers. This opportunity to be in a *giver* role emotionally can produce a significant change in self-concept.

Balancing a tendency to over-analyze

For people who are best at analyzing and discriminating, sitting provides a chance to do that without verbalizing it. In the silence sitters can notice that process, name it, and perhaps even feel the emotion that might be associated with it. They can notice when analyzing is a useful skill and when 'knowing' or 'understanding' or 'maximizing' might be an outdated defense against simply feeling and being in the mystery of the present.

Balancing a tendency to over-control

For people who acknowledge themselves as controlling, who often had very real need in childhood, or even in the present, to control

23

themselves and others in order to protect themselves, sitting is a time when there may be enough space to notice more clearly what is happening when such a need or impulse to control arises. The sitting role requires that one defer to the breather's inner healer— following and supporting, rather than controlling, pre-judging, or directing that process. Thus, if one's inclination to control arises, one is more likely to notice it, just because one is performing the function of sitter.

Balancing a tendency to over-support

People whose main inclination is to support, who tend to put their own needs aside, and who often behave co-dependently in relationships, will likely find most aspects of sitting familiar. They will probably learn more from the breather role. But still, the practice of sitting may teach supportive types how to empower a breather, rather than to enable or do the breather's work for them. It may also provide the meditative space to notice one's own co-dependent impulses. For example, if a person is crying expressively, it may be a new experience for such a person to allow someone to express those painful feelings fully, rather than to impulsively try to fix or comfort the person. In the Sharing Group such a person often will talk about how difficult it was to watch the breather's pain and remark how amazing it was to hear the breather express the value of such full expression after it was over.

Learning to sit with our own processes

In general, the practice of sitting in Holotropic Breathwork strengthens those parts of us that can act as resources when the rest of us is 'in process'. It strengthens our ability to act as our own internal Witness, commenting on, understanding, and mediating our complex emotional reactions. It also strengthens our compassion, the Nurturer part of us who can provide us with self-compassion, even in the face of our most virulent inner Self-Critic or Self-Blamer. Through our empathy with our breather, we also strengthen our connection to our own feeling, sensing, intuitive, or cognitive parts, resulting in our own greater integration. The practice of role-modeling the Witness during the intense process of a breather strengthens our own Witness self to be able to stay present during our own periods of intensity. The practice of role-modeling compassionate caring and service to a needy breather increases our ability to be compassionate with our own internal neediness.

Observing others gives permission

A sitter focuses on his or her breather, but sometimes a sitter widens his or her attention to see or sense what is going on with a breather nearby and sometimes broadens his or her focus to the whole room. I have often heard a sitter describe a similar experience to this one that Jack Silver describes in his first sitting experience:

> I looked up and was overwhelmed with emotion. My heart had opened up, and I was caring not only for my breather (my beloved), but the room as well. I felt I was sitting for the World. The joy, exaltation, pain and sorrow of the World flowed through me as I witnessed.[21]

When the focus is broadened in this way, the sitter also has the opportunity to discover what is possible, from watching other breathers. In other words, the sitter can learn for his own future benefit as a breather that the scope of permission and protection is quite large in Holotropic Breathwork, and that processes he or she may have suppressed need not be suppressed in future sessions as a breather. Likewise, learning occurs when the sitter works in a cooperative way along with the facilitator if the facilitator is providing nurturing touch to the breather. Nurturing touch (with the breather's request or permission) to the breather is given for a corrective experience of childhood omission. The sitter can learn also by assisting the facilitator with Holotropic Breathwork's special form of bodywork, designed to amplify the breather's body experience and help with integration at the end of a session. The sitter often learns from watching the facilitator work with breathers nearby as well.

Learning in Holotropic Breathwork applies to everyday life

Learning to sit with death, birth, grief, and major crises in ordinary life

Some Holotropic Breathwork participants have noticed that the practice of sitting prepares them to be with and to 'follow the process' as it unfolds in life outside of Breathwork sessions. Sitting seems to increase one's ability and willingness to sit with and flow with the changes of life. The most intense of those changes involve death and rebirth as it occurs in all its forms. Kathleen Silver and I, each independently, wrote about the preparation which the practice of Holotropic Breathwork had given us for sitting with each of our fathers as they lay dying.

Kathleen Silver writes:

> *About a year and a half ago, before my father died, he spent much of his waking time reviewing moments in his life where he felt regret. As he and my mother had then been living with us for almost two years, I was witness to many an hour of long, painful descriptions of what he essentially felt were personal weaknesses in his life. At first this review was grating and tiresome to me. I felt angry that he was 'negating' a life that I had always viewed as uncomplicated and filled with heart and wisdom. Thanks to a Saturday afternoon conversation with Jack Kornfield,[22] I soon was able to sit for my father, as I would in a Breathing session for a Breathing partner. I was able to understand that what he was in the process of doing was a life-review.... I began to encourage him to really open up his feelings about these moments in his memory and to talk to me about them. I did this mostly by asking questions. My intent was similar to that of the facilitator who is helping with bodywork*

during a Breathing session—encouraging, giving permission to one who might otherwise be too shy or private. When a person knows they will soon die, many of the things that would previously be concerns fall away, and the truth is much easier to speak. Interestingly enough, the things which angered my father most about himself were also the things which angered me most about my father—acts of omission. Fears that pulled him away from what he sensed were right actions. He was not mean; he was just silent. He gave me, as his sitter in the last few months of his life, one of the most important lessons in my life—that to be with someone in the fullest sense of the word, you must put yourself aside and listen and look with your heart. Through his pain, he also drove home the value of the lesson Joseph Campbell called 'following your bliss'.[23]

I wrote about my own experience with my father:

I simply could not have been there without the experience I have had over the years of sitting and breathing. Sitting with my father proved much more difficult than sitting in a Breathwork session. He was dying of cancer. The two weeks were one long Breathwork session.

My father was a man who had no metaphysical education, no New Age interests, and no afterlife illusions. He was completely surprised by intense, non-ordinary states of consciousness in his last weeks. At first he didn't know he was 'hallucinating', but he quickly caught on after a few days and actually became somewhat adept at it. He could go in and out of experiencing, then commenting in turn on the 'hallucinations'. He was having vivid visions and performing what seemed to be shamanic work. His eyes were focused intently and his hands moved constantly in the air before him interacting with various unseen symbols that appeared to have meaning in his life review....It was difficult to understand what these symbols meant to him. One thing about death is there is never a sharing group after the 'session' [as there is in Holotropic Breathwork] in which you find out what was going on. The symbols he mentioned were intriguing though, and sometimes I thought I could get an intuitive glimpse into his world. He saw and worked with lots of cords attached to things and vehicles. He spoke of paths, rooms, booths, bundles, and a television with switching channels. The work he was doing seemed important to him. We participated, or held his hand through fearful parts, or just sat quietly watching....

My father's process triggers my process. He is embodying my unresolved fear of pain and self-disappearance. I look at him and see his skeletal, wasted frame that will be soon traveling on the conveyor belt into the crematorium.

"Where am I going?" he asks me, raising up a little, his eyes locked with mine. I am ashamed not to know, but I admit it.

"I don't know," I said. "It is the Great Mystery." He sinks back. I think he agrees, but he is a little disappointed. I feel the present grief of missing him already in his ordinary state of consciousness and the anticipatory grief of missing him forever.

Now he asks us, "Should I go with them?" My brother eagerly inquires, "Who?" My father does not respond. So I venture, "Can you trust them to lead you?" "Trust them?" he wonders. "Yes, I guess so. That's a good idea." And for the moment he relaxes.[24]

Learning to sit with change and ultimate death in one's own life

Skill in sitting is of use in caring for friends. The skills and focus of sitting are practical, maybe even crucial, in parenting and grandparenting. The final place where we will use our practice of sitting is in sitting with our own loss of self and the change involved in giving up our bodies and life as we know it. The practice of sitting with another's pain, fear, grief, and loss of control in the face of transformation is the practice that will give us the skills we will need ourselves in facing our own final moments.

When a friend had an acute episode of spiritual emergency, Ray Kelly used his sitting and facilitating skills to work with the situation. He wrote, "I had a major 'ah-ha' experience....I finally realized that the Grof Transpersonal Training modules were segments of 'life' and not Breathwork as a separate experience. Prior to this, I had unconsciously segregated them in two distinct places. It dawned on me that the 'container' was never meant to hold the lessons forever."[25]

Learning to move beyond co-dependence in relationship

One of the really useful practices of the sitter/breather relationship is the practice of reciprocity. The sitter's role is to give whatever support the breather requests (or to call the facilitator if uncomfortable with a specific request). The sitting role is to give, to put the focus on the breather, the other. If there is a conflict between one's own needs and the breather's, one generally tries to accommodate the needs of the breather—the one who is in process.

On the other hand, when one moves into the breather role, one is focused on receiving. The breather is specifically not responsible for the needs of the other, the sitter. So if a breather is co-dependently thinking that it might be too much to ask the sitter to hold her hand or get her a drink of water, the breather knows that such thinking is her own process. The breather's job is to ask for what he or she needs to facilitate the process, not to worry about the sitter's reaction. Conversely, the sitter's role is not to take personally any request or action by the breather who is 'in process', but just to support the breather's process with an attitude of surrender and service.

This learning is transferable to ordinary relationships outside of Breathwork. One couple I know learned through the clarity of the breather/sitter roles how to distinguish who of them was in process and who would be assisting. When it seemed as if they were both in process at the same time, they clarified it verbally. If they were both in process, they alternated roles of 'breather' and 'sitter' by passing a talking stick[26] object back and forth. Whoever held the object was the 'breather' and the 'sitter' listened attentively until the object was passed back again.

Asking for what one wants (assertiveness)

If the sitter has an attitude of service, the breather can begin to surrender to being served. Part of that is to begin to be able to ask for what he or she wants—to actively participate in the receiving end of the 'give and take' of life. Many people don't know clearly what they need and want. Some who do know what they want, don't think it would be possible or appropriate to get it. Even if they do know what they want and think it would be possible to get it, they sometimes have great difficulty in asking.

The biographical material which arises during a Holotropic Breathwork session usually dissociated itself during an intense experience. No matter whether the experience was 'positive' or 'negative', it went into the unconscious and, and waited until it had the right conditions that provided another human presence and corrective conditions for healing. Somehow the inner healer recognizes when it is time, and the material comes forward. At that point our task as breather is to sponsor the material so that it can be embodied and integrated.[27]

The breather has very few 'duties'. The breather lies down in an open body position, breathes faster and deeper than usual for an extended period of time, cooperates with what arises, and (importantly) asks for what he or she wants and needs to support the process that emerges in the non-ordinary state. The practice of performing that 'duty' to ask for what one's inner healer requires can result in the repeated and corrective experience of being cared for in the way that one needs and wants. It also can have the side benefit of training one in assertiveness. The sitter, who by his or her receptiveness and caring, encourages the breather to do these things, learns how to empower another person.

Saying no to what one doesn't want

Saying no is as important (sometimes more important) in assertive behavior as asking for what one wants. In Breathwork many people relive situations in which as a child or adult they felt afraid to say no and felt helpless to set a boundary.

In a Breathwork session, even if a person asks for something (*e.g.,* wanting the sitter to hold a hand), there will come a time, further on in the session, when the breather doesn't want to hold that hand anymore. For some people it is a real benchmark to be able to tell someone to stop touching them, or even to "Let go of my hand," especially if they know the sitter is enjoying being helpful and connected. The role of breather gives permission to experiment with saying "No!" and to set those boundaries.

Breathwork can be a practice in differentiating oneself (and what one wants) from the other (and what the other wants). In the process of practicing this, breathers grow to trust the inner healer and honor their own inner impulses. They feel growing confidence in the basic right to set boundaries with their own bodies and psychological processes. From time to time sitters may feel rejected when a breather says what he or she doesn't want. This can be an opportunity for a sitter to learn how to let another person have his or her process, to not take that process personally, and to look at one's reaction to "No!" as one's own process.

Summary

Holotropic Breathwork as a meta-practice

Martin Boroson makes the case that Holotropic Breathwork is a meta-practice for the breather, providing a container so large that it contains any experience from any spiritual or psychological system or practice.[28] For example, one might enter the holotropic state and experience deep mystical states, or have a kinesthetic spiritual experience with automatic yogic postures or spontaneous sounds. One may have imagery from not only the major religious traditions, but also from smaller sects or from shamanism in all its ethnic forms. It is also possible to have, in a spontaneous way, many of the healing experiences that occur in traditional psychological therapy. Boroson writes:

> *Holotropic Breathwork, free to meander everywhere and anywhere across this spectrum, brings us directly to the cutting edge of our evolution. It requires only that we lean toward the truth that is emerging now and here, in the deepest and farthest reaches of the present moment. With unprecedented openness—in theory and method—it embraces all the ancient forms of worship and all the modern means of personal growth, and even holds space for those paths yet to be invented. Through it, we can gain access to the entire spectrum of consciousness, to all the magnificent dimensions of Being, and we can travel along any or all of wonderful therapies and paths, aiming always, steadfastly, at the one, integral goal.* [29]

In Breathwork we tend to consider breathing as the practice. In this article I wanted to acknowledge the silent, but quite powerful partner in Holotropic Breathwork—sitting. Boroson describes Holotropic Breathwork insightfully as a meta-practice. Sitting as well as breathing is part of this meta-practice.

Sitters who are present and focused on relationship with their breather often experience, in ways appropriately unique to them, whatever they are next called to learn about themselves. Depending upon what needs developing or balancing, sitters may learn more about empathy, emotion, impulse control, dissociation, or their own value as people who can give something important to others. They may strengthen their internal functions of witnessing and nurturing, while providing care to others. They may learn to take turns with the giver and receiver roles in their own relationships. They may learn to broaden and intensify their focus of attention while practicing presence. They may learn at some point, as Ray Kelly did in his 'ah-ha' experience (above) that sitting cannot be contained in a Breathwork session, but flows out into 'ordinary life' as a greatly enhanced ability to be present to more of Life, more of the time. All of this practical and spiritual education comes respectfully, appropriately, and spontaneously in the meta-practice of Holotropic Breathwork, while sitting for another in relationship.

---

[1] Silver, J. (1999.) "Here I Sit." *The Inner Door*. Santa Cruz, CA: Association for Holotropic Breathwork International. 11(2) 1. Republished in Taylor, K. [Ed.] (2003.) *Exploring Holotropic Breathwork*. Hanford Mead Publishers, Inc.

[2] Ibid.

[3] Ibid.

[4] The word *ritual* is used here in its anthropological meaning.

[5] *Set* is the cognitive construct of the process; *setting* is the container in which the process occurs. Grof, S. (1980.) 307.

[6] Taylor, K, M-L Gould, and I. Pacey coined the phrase "protection, permission, and connection" in designing their model for the GTT module: *Trauma and Transformation*.

[7] Gilligan, S. (1997.) *The Courage to Love*. NY: W.W. Norton. 180.

[8] Taylor, K. (1994.) *The Breathwork Experience*. Santa Cruz, CA: Hanford Mead Publishers, Inc. 35.

[9] Gilligan, S. (1997.) *The Courage to Love*. NY: W.W. Norton. 180.

[10] Taylor, K. (1991.) "On Being Seen, Heard, and Touched." *The Inner Door*. Santa Cruz, CA: The Association for Holotropic Breathwork International. 3(2)5.

[12] Taylor, K. (1994.) *The Breathwork Experience.* Santa Cruz, CA: Hanford Mead Publishers, Inc. 35.

[12] Montagu, A. (1966.) *On Being Human.* New York: Hawthorne Books. 49-67.

[13] Taylor, K. (1991.) "On Being Seen, Heard, and Touched." *The Inner Door.* Santa Cruz, CA: The Association for Holotropic Breathwork International. 3(2)5. Republished in Taylor, K. [Ed.] (2003.) *Exploring Holotropic Breathwork.* Hanford Mead Publishers, Inc.

[14] Taylor, K. (2004.) "Self-Relations in Holotropic States of Consciousness: Articulating the Therapeutic Relationship in Holotropic Breathwork" in Gilligan, S. [Ed.] (2004.) *Walking in Two Worlds.* Zeig, Tucker & Theisen.

[15] Ibid.

[16] Sparks, T., *et. al.,* "Doing, Not-Doing." A monograph on "not-doing" in Holotropic Breathwork.

[17] Taylor, K. (2004.) "Self-Relations in Holotropic States of Consciousness: Articulating the Therapeutic Relationship in Holotropic Breathwork" in Gilligan, S. [Ed.] (2004.) *Walking in Two Worlds.* Zeig, Tucker & Theisen.

[18] *Vipassana* is a Buddhist practice of mindfulness.

[19] Taylor, K. (1995.) *The Ethics of Caring* is concerned with how these unconscious drives result in unconscious counter-transference in caregiving relationship and how caregivers can become conscious of fears, desires, and longings.

[20] The word *holotropic,* coined by the Grofs, means *moving towards wholeness.*

[21] Silver, J. (1999.) "Here I Sit." *The Inner Door.* Santa Cruz, CA: Association for Holotropic Breathwork International. 11(2)1. Republished in Taylor, K. [Ed.] (2003.) *Exploring Holotropic Breathwork.* Hanford Mead Publishers, Inc.

[22] Jack Kornfield is a Buddhist meditation teacher, founder of Spirit Rock Meditation Center and author of several books, including: *The Path with Heart* and *After the Ecstasy, the Laundry.*

[23] Silver, K. (1996.) "A View from the Window: Considerations about Life Review and Holotropic Breathwork." *The Inner Door.* Santa Cruz, CA: Association for Holotropic Breathwork International. 8(2) 1. Republished in Taylor, K. [Ed.] (2003.) *Exploring Holotropic Breathwork.* Hanford Mead Publishers, Inc.

[24] Taylor, K. (1996.)"Sitting with Life, Sitting with Death." *The Inner Door*. Santa Cruz, CA: Association for Holotropic Breathwork International. 8(4)2. Republished in Taylor, K. [Ed.] (2003.) *Exploring Holotropic Breathwork*. Hanford Mead Publishers, Inc.

[25] Kelly, R. (2001.) "Bringing the Work to Life." *The Inner Door*. Santa Cruz, CA: Association for Holotropic Breathwork International. 13(3)7. Republished in Taylor, K. [Ed.] (2003.) *Exploring Holotropic Breathwork*. Hanford Mead Publishers, Inc.

[26] A talking stick ceremony is a Native American process in which the ritual object is passed to a speaker and all others in a group listen, without interruption to the person who holds the object until that speaker is finished.

[27] Taylor, K. (2004.) "Self-Relations in Holotropic States of Consciousness: Articulating the Therapeutic Relationship in Holotropic Breathwork™ in Gilligan, S. [Ed.] (2004.) *Walking in Two Worlds*. Zeig, Tucker & Theisen

[28] Boroson, M. (1998.) "Radar to the Infinite." *The Inner Door*. Santa Cruz, CA: Association for Holotropic Breathwork International. 10(4)5-7. Republished in Taylor, K. [Ed.] (2003.) *Exploring Holotropic Breathwork*. Hanford Mead Publishers, Inc.

[29] Ibid.

~3~

Yogic Sleep and Meditation States during Holotropic Breathwork

[First published 1991 in The Inner Door, *3(1)5, 7 and republished in Taylor, [Ed.] (2003.)* Exploring Holotropic Breathwork.)

Sometimes people will arrive at the group sharing with either no mandala, or a beautiful mandala, and a report that they have no idea what happened.

"I must have fallen asleep," they offer wistfully, after hearing the vivid stories of the other participants. There is usually a belying radiance about them, and upon further probing, they usually do report a feeling of serenity and a sense that 'something' happened—they just don't know what.

My theory is that such people are experiencing one of the meditation states which have been described by very specific Sanskrit terms for thousands of years. I have begun to include a reference to these states in the Introductory Talk along with the descriptions of other possible holotropic experiences. I usually say something quite simple, such as:

"Sometimes the inner wisdom decides that the conscious, censoring mind needs to be turned off in order for some kind of healing to occur below the level of consciousness. People often think they have fallen asleep, but it is practically impossible to breathe heavily for an hour and then fall into ordinary sleep. When we have observed people during a such a 'sleep' episode, we have noticed that their breathing pattern is unlike normal sleep. Yogis have identified many meditation states that are called by Sanskrit names to differentiate them from ordinary sleep and from each other. It is not necessary to have a dramatic experience or even to remember one's experience to have had a profound and healing experience."

When participants are reminded about this statement after actually having such an experience, it usually provides sufficient reassurance for people that 'something happened' and that their own experience was an important one.

Some people, however, want to know even more about the yogic sleep/meditation states. Whether or not they have conscious memory of their experiences, some of the information below, taken from Kripalvananda's book[1] may be of interest to some Holotropic Breathwork participants.

Tandra—Yogic drowsiness is experienced in meditation and is different from a tired drowsiness. When *prana*, life energy, begins to be released, the body becomes further relaxed and loose. Yawns come in quick succession. This often appears to be happening in Holotropic Breathwork as people cross the threshold between ordinary and non-ordinary consciousness and need to be reminded by their sitters to breathe. The increased prana drives the external organs or limbs to perform numerous movements. After the external organs become fatigued and inactive, the prana begins to do subtle work in the internal organs.

Yoga Nidra—This means *yogic sleep*. After the external organs have moved and become fatigued, the prana becomes stabilized and generates a state called *yoga nidra*. This is a state which may be experienced in meditation, during the night, or in a nap as part of sleep, but is not ordinary sleep. The mind is deeply introverted. If it is a very deep state, there are no thoughts or dreams. If it is not so deep, there are dreams, but the mind remains more focused than in ordinary dreams. In a *yoga nidra* dream there is concentration on detail in the dream and the 'action' of the dream moves very slowly and vividly. It does not flit from one scene or topic to another. In deep yogic sleep after the release of prana, the mind is not attached to the body or to prana and can rest deeply. Its main characteristic is very slow breathing. It may be so slow, it seems to have stopped, but it does not fully stop. This state comes on slowly and leaves slowly.

Murcha—This means *swoon*. Ordinary swoon is a physical disorder. Yogic swoon occurs when the prana tries to move up through the body and hits a blockage. As meditation (or Breathwork) practice continues, the energy passages through the body are gradually cleansed and the swoon state no longer occurs. A high degree of spiritual concentration is required before anyone experiences swoon. There are two kinds (below).

Videhalaya—is *murcha* in which there is no physical awareness, only identification with the astral body.

Prakritilaya—is *murcha* in which there is no physical or astral awareness, but only identification with the causal body. In both *videhalaya* and *prakritilaya* there are no thoughts, dualities, and desires. The breathing process in *murcha* comes to a sudden halt, not gradually as in *yoga nidra*. And the person returns to consciousness suddenly as well. All ordinary thoughts, dualities, and desires return as well, when the swoon passes.

Jada Samadhi—In this state the body remains static and the mind becomes unconscious. It is closer to swoon than *samadhi*. The body is locked into one position if sitting, whereas in *murcha* it would fall down if sitting. The mind is even more concentrated than in *yoga nidra*.

39

Sabija Samadhi—This is a very high level of meditation where there is no loss of consciousness, and there is very slow breathing. The mind and the prana still exist.

Nirbija Samadhi—This is the highest level of meditation where the mind and the prana dissolve and there is only Consciousness. The breath may stop completely.

―――――――――――

[1] Kripalvananda, S. (1977.) *Science of Meditation.* Bombay, India: New Karnodaya Press.

~4~

Holotropic Breathwork Adjunct to Substance Abuse Treatment in a Therapeutic Community

[Presented by Kylea Taylor and Steve Macy at the 1993 conference of the Association for Holotropic Breathwork International in San Francisco, California. The epilogue was written in 2006 and the manuscript was edited by Kylea Taylor in 2007.]

Applicability of Holotropic Breathwork to Addiction Recovery

Research procedures

We have offered Holotropic Breathwork™ sessions periodically since September 1991 in the Therapeutic Community of Sunflower House, In Santa Cruz, California. A certified Holotropic Breathwork facilitator, who is also a regular part-time staff coordinator, conducts the sessions with the help of one or more of the coordinators on staff. We use four questionnaires to collect data from the participants. A participant fills out a *Pre-Questionnaire* before participation, a *Same Day Questionnaire*, which is a descriptive questionnaire after the Breathing experience, a *Two-Week Post-Questionnaire* given two weeks after Breathwork, and a *Final Post-*

Questionnaire as the participant moves to the job search phase of the program. All questionnaires self-rate the participants' current impulses to drink or use drugs, their level of impulse to complete (or leave) treatment, and their degree of closeness to other members (peers in treatment). The *Pre-Questionnaire* asks for demographic data, pre- and post-natal information, trauma history, and for a rating on the importance of religion and spirituality in the participant's life. The *Same-Day Questionnaire* asks for a narrative of the participant's experience. The *Two-Week Post-Questionnaire* asks about the impact of the Breathwork experience on other aspects of the participant's treatment and life (was the Breathwork experience mentioned in conversations with a coordinator, in groups, in dreams, etc.) The *Final Post-Questionnaire* asks participants to check which kinds of Breathwork experiences they experienced during the session(s) in which they participated.

There were 56 participants in this study, who breathed an average of 2.1 times during the study. At the beginning of the data collection, it was considered voluntary to fill out a questionnaire, so in many cases, some of the follow-up questionnaires are missing. The *Final Post-Questionnaire* was administered when members entered the point in program where they were training to seek employment and were no longer available for most other structured program activities. Since many members left treatment before getting to that phase (which begins after 12-15 months of treatment), they did not fill out a *Final Post-Questionnaire*. Therefore, only nine respondents completed the final checklist of all the kinds of experiences they had in all of their Breathwork session. However, the descriptive reports from the checklists on the *Same-Day Questionnaires* have been very helpful in formulating the observations in this paper.

We have not done any comparison between those members who chose to breathe and those who chose not to. This could be another study.

Description of participants

Sunflower House residents have the following characteristics: 92% are referred by the criminal justice system and 80% of the members are there because treatment is their only alternative to imprisonment. A resident has, on average, used heroin, cocaine, or alcohol and other drugs, for more than 10 years. About half have finished a high school education. Ethnically, 65% are Caucasian, 16% are Latino; and 10% are African-American. Males make up 65% of the population; females, 35%. About half are over 30, a third are in their 20's and 13% are 18-20 years old. The average length of stay in treatment for those over 20 years of age is six months.

There are no figures for other data on the Sunflower House population, but the U.S. statistics for residential drug clients shows that 60% had engaged in predatory criminal activity in the year prior to admission (e.g., burglary, robbery, auto theft, or forgery). The primary income of 34% of residential drug clients was from an illegal source (e.g., drug sales, prostitution, or gambling.) Only 15% were engaged in legitimate full-time employment in the year prior to admission. Other figures in this national study show that 63% of residential clients reported symptoms of depression in the year prior to admission, 44% reported suicidal thoughts and/or suicide attempts, 28% exhibited anxiety disorders, and 26% exhibited mood disorders. Although Therapeutic Communities do not diagnose personality disorders in their members, most clients do exhibit symptoms of some type of personality disorder (e.g., antisocial, borderline, passive-aggressive, paranoid, obsessive-compulsive, self-defeating.)

In the portion of the Sunflower House population which volunteered to participate in Holotropic Breathwork, 78% were Caucasian; 18% were Latino and 5% were Afro-Americans. Males make up 61% of the Breathwork participants; females, 39%. During our eighteen-month study period, 55% of all residents who breathed have stayed clean and sober and remained outside of the court system. Of those who have left treatment during this time period, 27% have remained clean and sober and outside the court system.

The Therapeutic Community (TC) modality

Therapeutic Communities have a relatively long history when you consider the history of therapy in the modern world. The first examples of TCs were seen on the two coasts of the United States in the early 1950's. On the East coast, L. Yoblansky was working with addicts at a hospital in New York, while in Santa Monica, California, Charles Dietrich was putting together Synanon.

Both men discovered that a form of therapy that involved one addict relying on another addict for guidance in getting away from drug addiction was quite successful. The antisocial "But don't ya' know I'm different" type of person, who often is drug-addicted and involved in the criminal justice system, inspired the development of a peer support methodology. An addict (now clean from drugs for some period of time—one hour or one year) would help the next addict. That addict would then stay clean and be available to help the next one and so on. The eventual outcome was a community where people moved from self-destruction to positive, healthy productive citizenship.

Yoblansky, a traditionally-educated psychiatrist, approached the development of this model from a clinical position. Dietrich's position came from the personal desperation of his own addiction. The short history is that the two men met and formed a union that gave birth to a form of powerful therapy. The concepts of TC work quite well to create community that provides a corrective experience for its members *if* under good management, but some TCs have perpetrated abuses on residents and allowed abuse of power by staff and older residents and had instances of gender inequalities (which were still culturally accepted in the 1960s and early 1970s). There was even abuse of female members, and this was also much more prevalent then in therapeutic and contexts of all kinds. Some TCs have been termed 'cults', and abuse by the founders has even been alleged. If the concepts of TC work are followed, if the vulnerabilities to the abuse of power are addressed, and if the quality of staffing, training, and supervision is high, good outcomes can occur. In terms Holotropic Breathwork uses often, TCs have, under these circumstances, achieved good "set and setting."

To put TC therapy in perspective, one should remember that, as recently as the late 1960s and early 1970s, addicts and alcoholics were still being treated right beside the mentally ill by lock-down, straight-jacket, and with the powerful tranquilizer, Thorazine. Addicts, along with other mentally ill persons or persons characterized as social deviants, were traditionally 'treated' by incarceration. Even today we 'treat' most addicts/alcoholics by incarcerating them.

The TC is a community, a microcosm within the greater community. TCs have a lineage unique even in addiction treatment. For many years none of them was involved with the 12-Step Community. Now, some have successfully integrated 12-Step activities and traditions into their programs. Sunflower House is a program that incorporated 12-Step traditions into the TC modality.

Despite this adaptation, TCs are a subculture with their own behavior modification systems. Privileges, such as freedom of movement, are given for rewards as an individual moves through four echelons within the TC. Some TCs have their own monetary systems. Much of the language (jargon) and other processes are standard from one TC to another. Some aspects are completely unique to one specific TC.

Treatment within a TC involves responsibility—responsibility for oneself as well as responsibility for other members and the environment itself. Addicts generally are thought of as irresponsible. The TC does not accept that concept. Addiction paradoxically requires that addicts be responsible—addicts must feed and be responsible for their drug habits. The habit is like a pet or child that must be cared for with consistent action. Drug habit analogies include: 'monkey on my back', or '2,000 pound gorilla'—even 'the dog'. This 'pet' must be fed several times daily. Addicts have paraphernalia to maintain, dealers and partners to appease, etc. With this kind of experience, the Therapeutic Community assumes that the addicted person does indeed know how to be responsible and does not accept less. The TC helps addicts change from being responsible for their drug or alcohol habit to being responsible for themselves as productive members of community.

TCs are operating throughout the world, from Australia to Japan to Europe. The TC, which operated as a rather autocratic, isolated, sub-cultural system in the 1950s and 1960s and early 1970s has changed to a much more democratic, consensus model, responsive to the larger community of society. Today's TC is most often tied into the local political system, and even dependent on public grants. It is therefore a much more open and politically responsible institution than it was in the past.

Society at large has been amenable to TCs, because society has a perennial frustration with drug addiction, alcoholism, and the criminal liability that society experiences as a consequence. TCs produce results. They can be effective even with people who are repeat offenders, who have long histories of drug and alcohol abuse, and who have been in treatment unsuccessfully several times previously.

The community of the TC is the change agent. Residents are 'members' of the community, and that status is what is therapeutic. Members not only run the program by managing many administrative duties, they also cook the meals, do the shopping, participate in fundraising, and work with each other by giving honest feedback, helping each other devise their own treatment plans, and participating in all activities. The staff ("coordinators" rather than "counselors") assists with personal treatment plans, daily interaction between members, attention to individual behavior, and group facilitation. There are many types of groups, including seminars, confrontational groups geared toward behavior modification, and groups facilitated to deal with deeper, suppressed anxieties and memories. At Sunflower House there is a 'personal focus' group, 'rage work', and psychodrama.

Similarities in philosophic approach between TCs and the practice of Holotropic Breathwork

Holotropic Breathwork is based on the premise that the "*inner healer* manifests therapeutic wisdom which transcends the knowledge that can be derived from the cognitive understanding of an individual..." The TC also subscribes to the notion that an individual has the ability to change and grow. Neither system categorizes people under pathological labels or diagnoses based on their behavior; they both simply describe the behavior. Both systems acknowledge that there are valid reasons for past or present experiences and behavior. The TC reason is that addiction is a disease. Holotropic Breathwork's reason is that there has been trauma at various stages of life. The TC advocates more awareness and change in thinking and behavior patterns during ordinary consciousness. Awareness is increased externally by peer support and feedback in TC. Holotropic Breathwork suggests that it is also advantageous to become more conscious of deep, unresolved life themes. These themes or patterns, while still unconscious, may control emotions, thought, and behavior. Greater consciousness of these levels comes from internal experiences during non-ordinary states of consciousness (NOSC).

Persons may initially use drugs and alcohol to achieve non-ordinary states of consciousness in pursuit of spiritual experience. Andrew Weil (1972) said in his book, *The Natural Mind*, "every human being is born with an innate drive to experience altered states of consciousness periodically to learn how to get away from ordinary ego-centered consciousness." The title for Christina Grof's book about addiction, *The Thirst for Wholeness* (1993) is taken from a quote by Carl Gustav Jung which implies the same innate drive. Holotropic Breathwork is a natural method for entering these states without drugs, thus it is a particularly appropriate technique for those in recovery.

The ten opportunities for enhancing the treatment of substance abuse using Holotropic Breathwork

Holotropic Breathwork is offered as a voluntary adjunct to treatment because certain elements in the Holotropic Breathwork technique seem to offer the opportunity to effect deep and lasting change. Holotropic Breathwork presents the following opportunities which are particularly appropriate to the healing process of addiction recovery.

1. The opportunity to enter non-ordinary states of consciousness to seek healing and wisdom, using a natural, non-addictive method

Residents are in no way obligated to participate. We let them know that their participation is completely voluntary. Their decision to participate or not to participate does not affect their standing in the therapeutic community.

A two-hour seminar describing Holotropic Breathwork is a pre-requisite for participation by members. The seminar includes a list of the contraindications. We ask participants to sign a form saying they have received information about the work, and that they do not have one of the conditions contraindicating Holotropic Breathwork.

The breath, rather than an external substance, is the catalyst for entry into the non-ordinary state of consciousness. At first talking about the non-ordinary state can be triggering for some addicts in recovery. More information about the long tradition of non-ordinary states in shamanic healing and the search for human wisdom usually makes Breathwork an exciting prospect in a new search for natural methods of healing and wisdom. Breathwork is so much work, we tell them, that it is not something one becomes 'addicted' to doing.

2. The opportunity for a direct experience of one's Higher Power

Many of the experiences which occur during Breathwork provide this kind of healing contact. Some participants experience a peak experience or mystical state; some experience a sense of purpose in life; some experience a new level of trust and gratitude. Some experience the mystery and grace of spirit/mind/body healing.

M/F who experienced deep meditation—44%

M/F who felt unity with all—11%

Here are the descriptions of nine different participants who had some connection with the spiritual during Breathwork.

It helps me put my recovery in a larger perspective.

I want to do Breathwork, because it keeps me in touch with my Higher Power, and that is what I need.

I feel I learn something each time, not only about myself, but about humans in general. It also helps to release or bring things up I have stuffed down so tightly.

I next felt a great surge of what I would like to regard as higher emotions of love, sorrow, and a sense of selfless longing.

Each session has been fulfilling in itself and has carried over into my daily existence. I find the sessions enjoyable for themselves as well as helpful to me in clarifying my beliefs and objectives.

It was all about forgiveness from my daughter and my ex-wife. I feel all the pain and misery I've been feeling since they left me is behind me now, and I don't have to dwell on it anymore. I tortured myself for long enough. I'm ready and willing to do recovery, and I am extremely grateful!

I saw a big yellow flood of color. It kept on coming back. After 10 or so floods of yellow, I saw black blotches being released from me. They were leaving me. This was symbolic to me. It was like the Lord filled me with yellow peace, and it in turn got rid of the black evil inside.

Somehow even though nothing extremely earth-shaking happened, I feel that some sort of healing process is taking place.

I spent the rest of the time in a deep meditative state experiencing a profound state of peace with myself and the world. I gazed into the light within me and realized that therein lay the healing power.

It is common for participants who continue to do Breathwork regularly to experience a greater and greater degree of trust in themselves and in the unfolding of creation and their own evolution. This is embodied in their ability to internalize the meaning of the 12-Step prayer—the Serenity Prayer.

M/F who reported feeling trust in themselves - 22%

M/F who reported feeling trust in others - 33%

It should be noted that the anecdotal descriptions would indicate a much higher percentage of participants who felt their trust level increased during the Breathwork sessions. The above statistics are from the nine respondents to the Final Questionnaire. Here are the statements of three different participants regarding increased trust in the process:

> I trust myself now to relax and check in with myself. I trust the process.

> I believe it helped in allowing me to be adventuresome. It gave me the freedom to feel my feelings.

> I feel my Breathwork was a continuance of my last session. This experience was very serene and pleasant. I saw a closed door with a tremendous amount of light coming through the bottom. I felt quite content. I felt some resolution regarding my last Breathwork, because I experienced a lot of rejection and pain last time.

3. The opportunity to experience self-empowerment by using one's own breath for profound healing

Three elements of the Breathwork particularly work towards self-empowerment. The first is that the therapeutic result of the work comes, not from an external therapist or director. Instead, it comes from allowing the inner self to bring forth the particular healing experience which is appropriate each time. The second element is similar. The catalyst for the inner journey is not an external one (e.g. hypnotist, therapist, or substance), but the natural, internal one of one's own breath. The third empowering element is that Holotropic Breathwork expects the participant to switch from being the 'helpee' (breather) role to the 'helper' (sitter) role. This role change communicates that 'who is helped' and 'who helps' is determined by the situation and not by expertise, degree, or some other innate role definition. One is able to get fully into one's emotions and then to be fully available and present the next day to assist another. One learns she or he does not have to be 'stuck' in one life role either as a giver (co-dependent) or as a receiver (e.g., victim, addict, or identified patient). Role flexibility contributes to an increase of empowerment and a decrease in helplessness and sense of victimization.

In addition, the members learn to switch perspectives from ordinary reality to non-ordinary reality, from process-oriented and transpersonal psychological techniques to behavioral/cognitive ones. They do not seem confused by this, because the ritual and the structure of Holotropic Breathwork clearly define the boundaries between the modalities.

> *During these couple of weeks after the session, I have realized the simple concept of letting myself feel what I need to feel and learn what I can and then let it go before something else happens, and I add it on top of what has already happened. Pretty soon, if I do not let go, I hold onto everything and it all builds up, and I become angry, overwhelmed, stressed, hurt, negative, confused, and stuck in the problem. It takes me a long time to get out of that nasty negative slump when I get into it. I have learned and have been practicing letting go, and feeling what I need to feel instead of holding onto it.*

4. The opportunity for physical and emotional catharsis of stress and trauma by resolving past issues

> *Often when someone had a deep or psychodynamic experience, there is no need for lengthy group discussions, sharing, or analysis. The protagonist has*

learned about the mystery of the problem in action,
and he or she feels better. ~ Yablonsky

Prior to Breathwork in Sunflower House, the whole staff would do "dissipations" with one member at a time. Originally this type of planned marathon psychodrama emerged because of a coordinator's spontaneous response to a member within some other type of group. For example, a dissipation could involve a member working out suppressed anger with his father through some transference to another member or staff member who resembles his father. The normal routine of the program was suspended during these dissipations. The staff worked with only five members over the three-day period with a 'shepherd' to help them. In this time period, they were given the opportunity to rid themselves of all secrets, anxieties, and repressed guilt. There was a standard procedure to guide members through this process. It was a staffing nightmare—difficult to facilitate, difficult for staff to recover from. The majority of the members were left out of the process.

Holotropic Breathwork replaced dissipations in Sunflower House. It fulfills the function of dissipations by offering permission and protection for full physical and emotional catharsis as appropriate. It makes effective use of staff time and gives the opportunity for one-third to one-half (14-18) of all members (rather than merely five members) to participate at one time. Holotropic Breathwork takes six hours a day during two days every 4-6 weeks (rather than three 24-hour marathon days). The regular program structure continues for the rest of the members (rather than being suspended as was the case during dissipations).

During the dissipations, the catalyst for non-ordinary states was lack of sleep and confrontation with emotional triggers such as pictures of family and planned psychodrama. In Holotropic Breathwork, the emotions needing release can be accessed more easily and with less wear and tear.

One man had not cried for many years. Paradoxically, he tried to control the emotions which were arising by breathing very hard for almost two hours. The way he approached his Breathwork session was the same as the way he approached his recovery in general.

> I breathed very hard for as long as I could. After what seemed an hour, nothing had happened as far as visions were concerned. I was disappointed. I had really looked forward to the experience. I felt as though I did it wrong or didn't have the ability to do it at all. The facilitator asked if that was kind of how my life has been in general: to try so hard to make things right and somehow they just don't work out. When I thought about it for a moment, it was as if a light came on inside my head, and I realized that it was exactly the way it was. I suddenly felt incredibly hurt and, I guess, sorry for myself. Whatever the reason was, I was in pain and reacted with something that's totally foreign to me: crying. I can't remember the last time I actually cried about anything. I was so in touch with a real feeling of pain and sadness, that I wasn't really concerned about what I looked like. That alone is way out of the ordinary for me. How I look to other people has always been top priority to me. When it was all over, I felt great! Emotionally, as well as physically. That feeling lasted for a few days at least.

Another had a similar experience which also felt like a mirror of his overall recovery process.

> Today I experienced some of the most intense pain of my life. It didn't seem like it would ever go away. I wanted to quit, but something inside would not allow it. The only option was to keep on breathing

	Ten Opportunities for Substance Abuse Recovery in Holotropic Breathwork*
1	The opportunity to enter non-ordinary states of consciousness to seek healing and wisdom using a natural, non-addictive method
2	The oppportunity for a direct experience of one's Higher Power
3	The opportunity to experience self-empowerment by using one's own breath for profound healing
4	The opportunity for physical and emotional catharisis of stress and trauma in resolving past issues
5	The opportunity for bonding with others through the group sharing and the sitter/breather partnership
6	The opportunity to deal with themes of death and surrender, which are frequent and powerful issues for addicts because of drug overdoses, abortions, HIV/AIDS and other serious illnesses, crime, and encounters with the criminal justice system
7	The opportunity to experience a retreat period of inner reflection, which provides balance to the often highly structured, active lives of recovering addicts
8	The opportunity to get in touch with the body, to re-associate what has been dissociated, including feelings of pleasure and unfelt, unresolved traumas
9	The opportunity of permission for sound and movement, which facilitates self-expression and self-trust
10	The opportunity for insight, understanding, and acceptance of accountability for one's life and actions
	* These "Ten Opportunities" are republished here from Taylor, K. (1994.) *The Breathwork Experience* and were fomulated during Taylor's facilitation of Holotropic Breathwork at Sunflower House.

through the pain. Slowly after a time that seemed forever, the pain gradually left my body. I was so exhausted from fighting it, I finally surrendered to it. Right at this moment I feel sore, but calm and relaxed.

Others express their relief at discharging various emotions. Here are seven different participants' expressions:

It took me across the whole spectrum of my emotions from the most traumatic to the more pleasant. I was extremely skeptical going in, but very pleased after I came through the whole experience.

I felt a great deal of joy, I shed tears of joy, and felt that the energy in my hands I could give away, perhaps use in a healing capacity.

I started getting real frustrated and got a feeling of nausea. I told myself maybe I need to throw up, release something. Then I felt this huge voltage of energy, and a black burst came out of me. I felt like I did a 90-degree angle turn and floated down about five feet to my bed. I felt totally relieved, relaxed, loved, great, calm—just in heaven. I started verbally expressing my comfort with long deep sighs. It was just what I needed.

Breathwork has given me the strongest feelings I have ever experienced. It makes me feel like my feelings may be something I don't know about. I absolutely never thought that I could have any feeling, no matter what it was, have so much impact on me. I think that I have some hope that if being sober is feeling that strongly, I could enjoy it.

I feel it brings up a lot of stuff that is hidden deep down, that hurts a lot, and I don't want to face. I need Breathwork, because it works for me.

The first time, I experienced some feelings that I hadn't allowed myself to feel before, one of which was sorrow. I cried like I can't remember ever doing, and then, when it was over, I felt great. This time, I reached a place during the session where I felt at total peace.

Breathwork opens me up and gives me the freedom to connect with my inner feelings and not be afraid of how I look to other people. I got in touch with a lot of feelings and pain. I thought it was going to be hard, but when I did it, it was actually very easy.

Addicts and alcoholics have had notoriously traumatic childhoods. Addiction is a family disease. Alcoholism is a major factor in child abuse. Almost universally, addicts have much work to do in recovering from traumatic childhoods. We have collected the following statistics from the Sunflower House population.

Statistics

M/F who had alcohol or drug-abusing parent—65%

M who reported incest—24%

F who reported incest—41%

M who reported sex abuse by non-family member—24%

F who reported sex abuse by non-family member—64%

M who reported having been raped—9%

F who reported having been raped—60%

M/F who reported having had a severe illness—22%

M who reported having had a severe accident—53%

M/F who reported having had a near death experience—53%

M/F who reported another type of trauma—44%

Ivor Browne, an Irish psychiatrist (1990) now theorizes that psychological trauma is "unexperienced experience." He says there is much evidence showing that persons undergoing severe emotional or physical trauma employ defenses which block out unbearable pain. When next they have the opportunity to contact that blocked experience (usually in a spontaneous or induced state of non-ordinary consciousness), they do not "relive" the experience, but rather, actually "live" or experience the trauma for the first time. Lenore Terr, a child psychiatrist who wrote *Too Scared to Cry*, a study of childhood trauma victims, says that this blocking does not usually occur in sudden, one-time-only traumatic incidents, but is much more likely when trauma (such as incest or childhood physical abuse) occurs repeatedly over time.

Both psychiatrists agree that remembering, reliving, or "experiencing for the first time" is the most important part of the healing. Browne recommends Holotropic Breathwork for this work, along with the healing support of psychotherapy, group therapy, family therapy, hypnotherapy, somatic therapies, and behavior therapy.

Observations regarding administration and the treatment institution

At the time Holotropic Breathwork was introduced at Sunflower House, the two top administrators had already had powerful personal Holotropic Breathwork experiences. This made them strong supporters of Breathwork. It is hard to imagine that we could have been successful without such support from top administration. They arranged for all staff to participate in Breathwork before it was implemented in the program. All staff support it. When staff have participated in Breathwork, they follow the TC concept of staff/member community and breathe alongside the members.

Since Breathwork was implemented, women have stayed in treatment longer. It should be noted, however, that other program components aimed at supporting women in treatment were also added at same time, including a women's rap, all-female groups, and women's retreats. Near the end of this paper, there is a section which discusses further the difference between women's and men's needs. It does seem that the combination of additional women's groups and Holotropic Breathwork works well for the women at Sunflower House.

The administration has been unable because of budget constraints on the staff schedule to allot much paid staff time for staff to participate in Breathwork. The staff who are assisting in facilitating have not had much interest in participating in Breathwork on their own time, despite the fact that it is available to them free at the facility or for a 50% discount, which we offered as an incentive to them, at our public workshops. Therefore, the staff training is limited in that they are missing the essential experiential sessions. They do not have much personal knowledge of different kinds of Breathwork experiences, which gives a different perspective on how to work with someone having such experiences. They are also missing the personal knowledge of how regular (non-drug) non-ordinary states can affect their own lives in a beneficial way.

5. The opportunity for bonding with others through the group sharing and the sitter/breather partnership.

TC members express experiences in non-ordinary states through art and oral sharing quite well. Their deep connection to the symbolic life shows as well in the way members do their mandala drawing. No one thinks, as participants in public workshops may, that the mandala part of the process is 'silly' or feels inhibited by lack of artistic skill. Without any instruction to do so, the sitters automatically began doing mandalas along with their breathers. Thus, everyone, sitters as well as breathers, has a drawing to share in the sharing group each day. They also spontaneously began sharing in pairs. After the breather shares, the sitter usually wants to tell (and the breather wants to hear) what he or she imagined the breather was experiencing.

Another indication of their intuitive gifts is that, quite often, the mandalas of the partners are amazingly similar. The sitter's sharing of images and impressions often reminds the breather of something he or she had forgotten to tell. All this work with images and intuition is validating to members who have not thought of these skills as valuable or practical.

Sitters at Sunflower House (unlike in a public session) seem more rarely to be distracted by their own thoughts or process during a session. The focus is: How can I assist my partner? Can I feel and know what they are experiencing? Sitters are often amazed at the degree of empathy they are able to feel.

6. The opportunity to deal with themes of death and surrender which are frequent and powerful issues for addicts because of drug overdoses, abortions, HIV/AIDS and other serious illnesses, crime, and encounters with the criminal justice system

Addicts have more experiences involving death and abuse. It is not surprising that this population seems to have more non-ordinary experiences that involve death and abuse than the general population. Many have seen several people die or be murdered. Many have lost friends and family members to illness, overdoses, alcoholism, AIDS, and accidents. Some have had experiences themselves of near death during an overdose or accident.

Experience of dying myself—22%

Experience of others dying—33%

Grieving for others—67%

Communicating with those who have died—22%

Reliving an accident—22%

Here are several examples:

> I went back to a time I thought I was going to die. I had eaten about 20 or more opiates, and I thought I was near death. My estranged girlfriend showed up and took one look at me and just shook her head. I tried to talk to her, and I could not move my lips. I had a complete reliving of that situation, and it hurt so bad. I was sick, itchy, sweating, and thought I was going to die. I do want to do Breathwork again.

> The one experience that really stands out is the one of death I had. It was like there was no way possible I was going to come back to life. There was a very empty and sad feeling inside of me when I awoke from the experiences. Over all I really enjoyed this session and look forward to doing it again.

> I saw my real father crash his airplane in the forest. I saw his best friend's secretary fall through the trees and live. She watched her boss and his best friend die. I felt like I was her and watched them burn and die. I cried a lot and told my Dad I loved him and called him Dad, because I never called him Dad. I said, "I love you, Dad" over and over until I know

*he heard me. Then I saw us hug and had an intense
feeling of love.*

*I was with my father as a young boy. He called me
the "Kiss of Death". We were yelling at each other. I
told him he was an asshole. When he died I went
and lay down on a cold slab with him, and I kissed
him and told him all the things I never could tell
him while he lived. I was sorry that I was not the
son he wished I would have been. Death seemed to
surround me.*

One man had a COEX (Grof's "condensed system of experiences")
experience that involved reliving a number of his own and another's
experiences of not being able to breathe.

*I remember feeling a hot piercing pain in my lower
right abdomen. I was stabbed once there and nearly
died. I began breathing real hard trying to get
through that pain. I felt myself beginning to drown
in pain, and the next thing I knew, I felt like I was
actually drowning in the ocean. I felt myself break
through the surface of the water and swam over to
my surfboard floating nearby. Then I was surfing
and felt the elation of riding waves. Then I took a
bad wipe out and the undertow kept pulling me
down, and I was running out of air. Things got dark,
and I felt an urgent need to breathe. Suddenly I
found myself giving CPR to a close friend of mine
who was dead. He was killed right in front of me in
Vietnam, and I had tried, futilely, to revive him. The
grief I felt then was unbearable, and until I relived
the emotion of that memory in Breathwork, I had
completely repressed that agony....Somehow our
patrol regrouped, and I relived running from the
enemy through the jungle. It was very hot, and I*

was terrified, and I finally hid in the bush until it got dark. I continued breathing very hard in the darkness, until I curled into a fetal position. My breathing slowed, and I became an embryo. I felt myself slide into a warm birth.

7. The opportunity to experience a retreat period of inner reflection which provides balance to the often highly structured active lives of recovering addicts

Participants learn the value of a retreat, a time to go fully into inner contemplation and to benefit from quiet, nurturing time with others. The subliminal message given is that the inner spiritual journey is important, and that it can be integrated successfully with external behavioral change in recovery. This is the cornerstone of 12-Step philosophy; in fact, the Big Book of AA says that without the spiritual awakening there is no recovery. In this retreat period after Breathwork, members are free to socialize with or get support from the other Breathwork participants. They may choose to go to bed early after a Breathwork session. This is a change from the usual 16+ hour day filled with tasks and structured activities. The retreat period supports the value of appropriate rest and reflection.

After Breathwork I have felt more comfortable with prayer and meditation.

8. The opportunity to get in touch with the body, to re-associate what has been dissociated, including feelings of pleasure and unfelt, unresolved traumas

Most addicts have been abused (see statistics above), and the number of those reliving abuse situations reflects this. Some (about a third) have had experiences that directly relate to their drug-using experiences. These may be not just events which occurred because of using, but even the physical feelings of using.

> *My arm hurt where I used to shoot heroin. Suddenly a burning streak of energy shot out from there through my hand and the pain was gone.*

> *I felt almost like I had received an injection of cocaine or something. It seemed as though all of my pleasure sensors had been stimulated. It felt good just to let go and to, well, feel good.*

Before doing Breathwork, most do not know much about their own births or about the experience of their mothers during pregnancy. The following are some data from the people who could answer the questions about their birth experiences:

Mother used drugs/alcohol while pregnant -12%

Mother was physically abused while pregnant -12%

There were birth complications -28%

Mother was anesthetized during the birth process -65%

It was a long labor -57%

Forceps were used -8%

It was a Caesarian birth -10%

They were breast fed -57%

It is not unusual for people to get more information about their own prenatal or perinatal experience while participating in Holotropic Breathwork. Here are two examples:

> *I was a baby still in my Mommy's tummy. I was completely safe; every inch of me was surrounded. I*

couldn't breathe through my nose. I was so warm and safe I could feel and hear my Mom's heartbeat. I was loved, totally. I kept getting tickled. Something tickled my side over and over. Some part of me thought my mother was having sex, and that was what was tickling me. I was starting to get born, but it stopped because I didn't want to go. I felt pains in my own uterus as my Mom was having pains. I never got born. I stayed safe, warm, and loved.

I felt as if I was all closed in and I was trying to get out. I began to scream out. I felt anger, hopelessness and hope. I felt as if I was afire. The top of my head hurt. Pressure was on the top of my head. I began to struggle like hell. I felt closed in, trying to get out of a hell hole. The more I struggled for my life, the better I felt. All of a sudden, I felt comfort. The facilitators were holding my head and back. I felt my heart beating against their hands of comfort. I felt a closeness to them as if they were my new Mom and Dad.

9. The opportunity of permission for sound and movement, which facilitates self-expression and self-trust

The following are four excerpts from the Holotropic Breathwork experiences of Sunflower House members as they relived old traumas:

I saw myself at nine or ten years old with my father who was drinking while I was taking care of him and keeping other family members out of harm's way. It was very realistic. My Dad was getting cut up by glass he broke. I was taking care of him. He was holding me while he was passed out, and I was afraid to move and wake him up. I was so many times in that situation.

I had the experience with my family when I was seven or eight when I had to go to my room. I did not know what I did wrong. I remember I was playing with my brothers and sisters, and I had done something wrong, so I went to my room. Then my Dad came in and started to hit me with a belt, and I was begging him to stop. I saw the gaze in his eyes. I was crying so hard that I forced myself in a closet, and I felt scared and nervous and uncomfortable. Now, I feel more strong than before.

I had a memory that I was abused by my father when I was six or seven. I remembered burning a gift he gave me in the back yard at that age because I was angry with him. Now I'm kind of putting things together, and I'm starting to believe it happened, even though I don't want to believe it. In my next session I was scared and angry at my father. I couldn't talk. I wanted to say, "Please, leave me alone!"

I was real emotional, remembering the deaths of my husband, Dad, and my son's father. I missed them. I have never cried for them. I realized I have to let them go. I also remembered when I got raped and felt those feelings. I was 16 years old. I have never put that out in group therapy. I felt a struggle between happiness and peace and being so sad. I want to do [Breathwork] again so I can understand my life.

10. The opportunity for insight, understanding, and acceptance of accountability for one's life and actions

Of the final (9) Breathwork questionnaires completed, 44% said they had a life-changing insight during a session, got a sense of their life purpose, and forgave themselves. A third said they also forgave others.

The Second through Ninth Steps of the Twelve Steps focus on this important part of addiction recovery. In the early stages of recovery, it is often difficult to feel the full impact of one's actions. The weight of guilt, sadness, and remorse is often too heavy to bear. The Breathwork enables the inner wisdom to choose its own time to make the truth known. Here are two examples:

> *I saw my friend when he was hit by a car. I left him lying there to die after the accident. I deserted him. I just dealt with regrets for my actions. Then I felt as if he was with me, watching me. When I was going through this pain, I saw him reach down and touch me on the heart. I felt his hand go through my skin and touch my heart. It was a pleasant soothing touch. In my next session, I saw him again, and I questioned whether he was in heaven or hell. He floated above my head, telling me everything is cool and all right. This whole experience was very resolving, very healing.*

> *I remembered after the session that I had re-experienced being pregnant and then my abortions. I remembered going to heaven and being given another chance for living life over again. God has forgiven me for my sins.*

The inner wisdom operating in non-ordinary states of consciousness has a broad view and seems to be trustworthy. It operates in a timely way for the greatest good. Although this is true in the broadest sense, the effects may not support short-term treatment goals. Short-term treatment goals are, of course, to keep the person continuing with treatment and sobriety in a particular program or in recovery. Addiction is a life-threatening disease. It is important to weigh a decision to participate in Holotropic Breathwork carefully. We know from the many stories of addicts that often something 'bad' has to happen in order for something 'good' to happen. 'Hitting bottom' is an example of this. Sometimes a Breathwork experience appears to have been at least part of the impetus for a member to leave program. There is always the question of whether a person was really ready to stay in recovery yet, or if they would have been ready to stay in recovery if they had not been challenged prematurely by such deep work. Here are examples from the *Same-Day Questionnaires* of two men who experienced great guilt in a session. They subsequently left treatment and returned to prison. One left three weeks after Breathwork, the other left one week after his session.

> *I experienced talking to my three children. One asked me why I keep using drugs and said, please won't I stop. One was crying. One told me I took 15 years out of her life by not being there, because I was always in jail.*

> *[Breathwork] brought up a lot of my feelings concerning my racial stuff and things I have done while in prison, things I don't feel comfortable having down on paper. I am undecided about doing it again.*

Often, however, in the Breathwork, a participant will have deep empathy for those they have injured. They experience accountability (Steps Four through Nine) in such a way that the truth comes with an overall sense of self-forgiveness and with acceptance of what cannot be changed. Here are four examples:

> *I saw all the people of my family I have hurt, then all the other innocent people. Then I saw all the pain I have put myself through by acting out. Finally I entered a peaceful state going over good memories*

and feelings. I feel this session has brought me closer in touch with some feelings (anger, pain, joy, and peace) of the past which I had blocked out for years. By getting in touch with these feelings and experiences, I know sharing, which completes each session, offers a setting for disclosure of intimate or mystic experiences. It provides a place to share these experiences, which are often outside the realm of ordinary consensus reality, with peers who have just had similar experiences.

I felt better than I had felt in a long time. I felt real connected with people in the house and I felt at ease with myself.

I do want to participate in Breathwork all that I can. It takes something bad out of me and leaves something good. My experience stays with me very vividly. I have real experiences in Breathwork. Breathwork is more real to me than I am to others. I like sharing my experiences with others. I like sharing my experiences with others at the end and on the floor. It is a time when I can be as real with other people as I am going to get these days. Other participants listen to what I have to say, and I listen to them. There is a closeness there that you have to experience to know.

I love the bonding experience that I get with my sitter and other participants that do Breathwork. I learn a lot about myself and others at the same time.

In a Therapeutic Community this can have a significant ripple effect. The Breathwork group has shared a profound experience together. They have experienced reciprocal nurturing. For the most part, they have respected and accepted each other's experiences without judgment or analysis.

Sitting for someone doing Breathwork was equally amazing to me. The first thing that struck me afterwards was how much closer I felt to my Breathwork partner—especially in light of the fact that I was not particularly close to (nor particularly fond of) that person going into the Breathwork. During the experience I felt a much deeper empathy with another person's emotions than I normally did, especially this person's emotions. Having come back to 'normal consciousness', I find myself becoming more attached to this person even though he continues to behave pretty much the same way he has since I've met him.

The whole structure of the Therapeutic Community supports peer bonding. The community undermines racial and ethnic prejudices of members, which usually have been annealed in the tense and rigid prison culture. Breathwork offers a particularly good opportunity for members to see the vulnerability and similarities they share, rather than the differences to which they have been taught to react. One of the nine *Final Post-Questionnaire* respondents said he felt unity with all, two said they felt compassion for others.

I still think about my first Breathwork experience. I frequently think about my last Breathwork, because it is exactly how I am today. Wanting to be close to people, but having a strong resistance to make a move towards that connection, even upon an invitation. Through Breathwork, I was on the outside, looking in on a barrier that I almost keep dear to me, and at the same time would like to break. I feel good about identifying what I felt. For some reason I feel good about what I felt.

It should be noted that there is also an opportunity for bonding among the members outside of the breathwork session who are supporting the Holotropic Breathwork participants (e.g., by cooking and staffing the desk, and by tiptoeing quietly by the Breathwork room all day). While this support section of the community attends to the tasks that keep the TC operating, powerful evocative Breathwork music is reverberating through the halls. The members who are not participating are constantly aware that they are supporting an opportunity for the others to work deeply. The trust and bonding from this style of group interaction complements and supports the TC work of confrontation and the stress of implementing behavioral changes via treatment plans.

M/F who felt very angry during Breathwork—67%

M/F who felt very sad during Breathwork—89%

M/F who felt emotionally healed—33%

M/F who reported emotionally charged imagery—22%

M/F who felt very good about themselves—56%

> *Breathwork helps me deal with real hard subjects for me to talk about, and it helps me release a lot of anger and tension built up.*

> *Every time I do Breathwork, more small pieces fall into place.*

> *It helps me remember stuff I avoid.*

> *I got rid of a lot of old luggage.*

Observations of TC members as participants in Holotropic Breathwork

They are less likely to move rhythmically during sessions

For over one year of doing these sessions, I puzzled over the fact that there was almost no rhythmic motion and little expression of sound in comparison to the general population which participates in Holotropic Breathwork. I have begun to think that this may be related to the previous experience these members have had with non-ordinary states. They have used drugs and alcohol in many unsafe situations. They have learned to control bodily and oral expression in order to protect themselves, always maintaining a level of hypervigilance.

Because the Therapeutic Community model focuses on changing behavior patterns, the members need to be as vigilant and in control while in treatment as they were on the street or in prison. The reasons for such vigilance are different. On the street or in prison they are hypervigilant in order to protect their physical bodies or to maximize opportunities to get high. In treatment this same vigilance is turned toward observing their own and others' behavior patterns—the ones which are not amenable to recovery—so that they stay clean and sober and are not returned to jail.

In the TC, members are to 'act as if', no matter how provoked, while participating in the ordinary structure of the program, except when they are in groups. Even in groups, certain rules apply regarding abstaining from physically violent gestures and verbal threats, and guidelines for how to process emotions.

There is a greater need to delineate boundaries

In Holotropic Breathwork, by contrast, the injunction is to surrender, to allow the body/mind to express spontaneously its long-held emotions (e.g., joy, pain, sadness, or rage.) I believe there is some difficulty for most of the members in making that switch between control of their behavior in ordinary consciousness and surrender to spontaneous healing processes in non-ordinary states.

For this reason, it is important to delineate the boundaries and differences between non-ordinary and ordinary states of consciousness. It is important to differentiate also between non-ordinary consciousness in an unsafe setting and non-ordinary consciousness in a safe setting. I have found it helpful to define and reiterate, just prior to each session, the switch in rules, permissions, and process (as above) which occurs with the start of a Holotropic Breathwork session. I also stress and enumerate the differences between a non-ordinary state experienced in an unsafe environment and a non-ordinary state experienced in the safe setting of a Holotropic Breathwork workshop.

We mark the boundaries also by the ways in which a Breathwork day at Sunflower House is different from a normal treatment structure. We encourage members to finish or delegate any ordinary responsibilities for the day before the start of the session. Blankets are put up to cover the windows, rugs spread over the floors, members move about the halls in stocking feet, we turn down the volume on the telephones, we whisper communications, we prepare special food, and we foster a retreat atmosphere with silence and a little incense. A short two-minute meditation begins the group as a way to shift awareness from the external to the internal experience.

Therapeutic Community (TC) members are excellent sitters

One of the differences in doing Holotropic Breathwork in the Therapeutic Community is that most of the members are excellent sitters. They already have a relationship with the person with whom they have paired, which explains some of the extraordinary quality of attention a member can give to a breather. They feel responsible to support each other in recovery. The Therapeutic Community teaches that, as human beings in community, we are all connected. I think the participants understand this connection and the sacredness of the work much more deeply than the general population of a public Holotropic Breathwork workshop.

The pattern of family dysfunction may return in the sitting triad

When there is an uneven number of participants in Holotropic Breathwork, three people partner together to form a triad. In one session there are two Sitters for one breather. In the other session, there is one Sitter for two breathers. It is always more difficult for anyone to sit for two people at once, but I think it can be more stressful to a person in drug treatment who already has difficulty in focusing and probably has a fear of 'not doing it right'.

This is what happens when a member sits for two other members in a triad formed because there is an uneven number of men or women. If one of the two breathers in the triad is quiet, that person has the possibility of becoming like the "lost child" role in the alcoholic family system. The attention goes to the one who is active or abreacting. The other needs less attention, or so it seems, and gets less. It is important for the facilitator to be aware of this and to be there when the quieter breather opens his or her eyes, in order not to reinforce those feelings of abandonment and invisibility and to provide a corrective experience of nurturing attention.

As I have watched these members in many situations, I see a quality of innocence and vulnerability that people who are not addicted to substances do not usually have. I have hypothesized that most addicts learned early to defend themselves emotionally with drug states and never learned some of the other defense mechanisms non-addicts have at their disposal. Without the drugs, addicts are relatively undefended and feel deeply many feelings which our modern society has taught us to deny.

TC members have more developed intuitive (psychic) skills

The ability to be in touch with one's intuition and allow communication with that intuition by symbolic vision is quite common in members. During the initial two-minute meditation at the beginning of each day's session, we instruct participants to do three things: (1) go inside and see how they are feeling in general and about doing the Breathwork in particular; (2) find a way to create a group feeling of cohesiveness in order to do this work together today; and (3) let a symbol come to them which has something to do with the two days' work. The same instruction is given in our public workshops. In the public workshops, roughly 20% are able to produce a symbol and to share it with the others. At Sunflower House, however, about 90% of the participants find it easy to produce rich symbolism (sometimes two or three symbols) and to articulate this imagery to the group.

> The whole group of us were sucked up into this rainbow tunnel and then we parachuted down into this circle with different colored parachutes.

> I saw two rings interlocked whirling through glass which shattered and shattered in slow motion.

> I saw a bent oval which, when it spun very fast, became round.

The length of time in treatment before participation in Holotropic Breathwork

How much should length of time in treatment enter into the decision to allow a member to do Holotropic Breathwork? If someone is newly clean and sober, can we trust the inner wisdom to select an experience which furthers recovery? Or might it bring up so much material, or such intense content that the person leaves treatment? How should we assess (and should *we* assess) who is ready and who is not ready to participate in a Holotropic Breathwork session?

At this point we believe that the voluntary nature of participation does much of the sorting. I have found usually that the two-hour informational video with its detail about the kinds of things that can be experienced will dissuade those who are not ready *before* they do it. Sometimes the word goes through the community that this is a real 'trip'. People can be attracted to it (1) to have a drug-like high; or (2) to show their fearlessness of 'trips' under peer pressure to participate. We are more alert now to those who are showing their bravado or machismo by volunteering to participate. If they are not yet wholehearted in their willingness to surrender and to explore, it may be best to postpone the Breathwork adventure. We encourage anyone who is hesitant to wait at least until the next scheduled Breathwork.

There have been a couple of instances of men who had been long-term inmates in prison who had very scary experiences and did not want to do Breathwork again. They have also left treatment. (See below.) Did these addicts reject both recovery and Breathwork because they were not ready to risk inner exploration, or did the Breathwork bring up too much, too soon?

We have become more alert to some of the warning signs that may mean we need to check with a person frequently after a session. For instance, someone may say at the end of a session *I didn't want to come back!* Again, this seems to indicate that returning to one's body and feelings in the present, in the real world, is too intolerable.

Low self-esteem

There may be some contraindications for allowing severely abused members with very low self-esteem to participate. In two separate instances, a male and a female member had peak experiences in NOSC in which they experienced very high self-esteem. They both said, "I didn't want to come back!" Each left the program within weeks of the Breathwork experience, after over nine months of residence. One might hypothesize that this was at least partly because it was difficult for them to reconcile their self-image in ordinary consciousness with their glimpse of their more whole or divine self. Perhaps the totality of who they were was too scary. Perhaps they craved the chemical substance which gives them a manageable portion of the divine while blocking out the self-hate temporarily.

One man had three sessions. In the first session he went back to what he felt was a past life over 100 years ago. He was a Native American warrior with high self-esteem who had a great love for his horse and the land and was under the care of a wise old man who was his teacher. He chanted in tongues (which he didn't remember afterward) and conducted a face-painting, and blood-letting ritual in pantomime during the session. In the second and third sessions he returned immediately to that time. In the time between sessions, he had returned to the past life in his dreams at night and had great difficulty with conflict between the despair of his current life and the fulfillment of the previous one.

> I tell (my teacher) I don't want to go back (to my real life). It scares me there. I feel I don't belong to anybody or anything here. This is not my time, or my home.... My soul looked at itself over 100 years ago and I cried. I've re-found what I've been missing for 35 years here. I have found me....I will ask my God to never send me back here again, for my soul is tired, and I need to be free from this body. Having to go through what has been my life up to this point has been disgusting, and very ugly and lonely. I feel this overwhelming urge to continue this Breathwork. Not for drug or alcohol abuse, but rather I have found my other self in a past life. I was beautiful there. I did not want to come back here. This has

*become an obsession to me. I need to know what
happened to me then, and why I am living life again.*

He left treatment suddenly, did some drinking, held a job for a
while, and was referred to another treatment program. At the
present time he is clean and sober, but has been court-involved in
the interim.

The woman also had three sessions. In the first two she had a
progressively explicit memory of horrible sexual abuse in early
childhood. In the last session she had an out-of-body fantasy
journey and a euphoric state.

*In my first session, I was back at aged two to six, I
felt what my uncles and grandpa did, how they did
it and why I hate the specific thing to this day. I hate
being touched that way. I felt myself scooting and
scooting, trying to get away, never saying anything,
as if it didn't matter. But it hurt over and over. I
hated it. I hate them. I cried when they left, but no
one knew. This has made me aware of a lot of
different thoughts. In my second session, the longest
part dealt with sexual abuse in detail with my
grandpa and two uncles. I was a very small tiny
child. I felt so little and confused. What they did
started out to be a game and continued on for 21
more years. They are alcoholics and got me
intoxicated and did what they wanted. My strongest
recollection was in the garage bedroom on my
grandpa's bed. They were all three there taking their
turns. I was tied with sheet strips to the bed head
with my head pressed against the bars. I could feel
the indentation on my head from the bars. They
would also one each hold my hands down. I
remember until they became numb. I was very cold
in that room. There was a window. One was always*

watching out of it to see if my Mom was coming back from the store where they sent her. I could smell that room and my Grandpa so distinctly. When I said to let go of me, my right arm, both of which were numb and paralyzed until then, was able to move and feel, so I was beating on the bed trying to hurt them. It wasn't pleasant, but it was good for me to go through to gain insight on what happened, how it happened, how it felt, and why I am what I am and treat persons the way I do. In my third session, I was out of my body, seeing everyone breathing including myself. Then I went from the center of the earth to the heavens. I was Earth, Sky, water, Being and Creation, seeing myself, feeling myself. Feeling power and worship, pain of death, self. Seeing and feeling growth of planet and self, with a feeling of care I thought I'd lost. It was a great experience.

She left treatment two weeks later. During the two weeks following her last Breathwork session, she crashed from her euphoria to despair and went from a responsible position in the facility to exhibiting relapse behavior. She left treatment. We have recent information that she has been imprisoned again for using heroin and/or prostitution.

Differences between men and women

Are women different than men in the kind of experiences they have in Breathwork, or in the support they need after Breathwork experiences? Some indications are that if women have left previous treatment, it may be because treatment has not addressed key issues, such as incest, or domestic violence, or has not addressed these in sufficient depth. In these cases, it may be appropriate for a woman to participate in Holotropic Breathwork early in this period of sobriety. At Sunflower House we do not yet have a thorough program providing incest survivor information. This would probably be a sound therapeutic complement to providing Breathwork experiences which bring up incest memories. One TC found that when they instituted a program of groups focused on incest issues, only one woman left treatment within a year's period.

Our statistics show that men were twice as likely as women to talk to their family or to one other friend about Breathwork experiences. Women, however, were three times as likely as men to use treatment groups to talk about the experiences, and twice as likely to talk to a coordinator or write about the experience in their journals.

The patterns of drug use in the backgrounds of male and female members are similar. Both men and women have used cocaine, alcohol, or heroin for over ten years on average. But there are some differences among their other traumatic experiences. Not surprisingly, women have reported incest at least twice as much. Women also report rape more than seven times as often (despite the fact that almost all of the men have been in prison where rape is frequent). Sixty-seven percent of the men had experienced physical abuse, 81% of the woman had.

The women seem to have different Breathwork experiences as well. Their predominant emotional experience was of feeling very sad (80%). And while 100% of the men (in the final nine questionnaires) experienced feeling very happy, only 60% of the women reported having that experience. While 67% of the men had relived positive childhood events, only 40% of the women had done so. Seventy-five percent of the men felt very good about themselves in the sessions, but only 40% of the women had felt that way. None of the women reported feeling compassion for herself or others, or reported feeling trust in herself or others.

Although these last data are only based on nine members' final questionnaires, they seem to dovetail with what we already know; women suffer from certain negative forms of gender socialization.

It seems important to use the women's willingness to talk in all-female groups to address the kinds of self-esteem problems that are sometimes brought to the fore in a Breathwork session.

Women who have breathed show a slightly higher percentage of success (59%) in sobriety than the men who have breathed (53%.)

Observations of other differences in facilitating Holotropic Breathwork in a TC

There are a few health issues which pertain more to this population than the general population. One needs to be more cautious about high blood pressure, even if it is currently controlled by medication. When addicts are using, they may receive no medical attention for their high blood pressure. If this continues for a prolonged time, as it may during the drug-using life, the arterial system can become weakened. It may be dangerous to participate in Breathwork, even after the blood pressure is eventually controlled by medication, because of the risk of strenuous activity to compromised arteries.

Extra attention should be given to the possible presence of communicable diseases, including tuberculosis and AIDS/HIV. Fresh air should be circulating in the room and rubber gloves should be available to sitters and facilitators when they are assisting with a breather's vomiting or mucous. The only two members with a known positive HIV status, who also participated in the Breathwork, left treatment. Both had experiences involving death in their Breathwork sessions, which they described as troubling and incomplete. Both declined to work further on these experiences and feelings in group. One went back to using heroin. The other is clean and sober.

A facilitator of Breathwork at Sunflower House needs to be flexible, because there are often last minute changes in the list of participants or to the scheduling of the Breathwork session itself. These changes can be due to: someone leaving the program, the need for program coverage (in the kitchen and on the desk); or some behavioral consequences for unacceptable behavior which may be given to individuals or to the whole community.

The best way to do an introductory talk in the facility is to do it 'live' with other members present who can speak about their Breathwork experiences. However, because of the lack of money for staff time, and the lack of open time in the structure of the program, this is usually not possible. The video serves the purpose of giving the information participants need. But people need to listen, and it is easier to pay attention to a live presentation than to one on tape. Also, without the Breathwork facilitator present, there is no opportunity to set the tone and to answer questions that arise on the spot.

Summary

Holotropic Breathwork provides an effective way of meeting many of the therapeutic goals for both the individuals and the community in a Therapeutic Community treatment setting. It provides a safe, contained opportunity for physical and emotional catharsis, for reliving and resolution of past trauma, for insight and understanding, for accepting accountability for one's life and actions, for self-empowerment, and for a deeper connection with one's Higher Power. The process between the sitter and the breather is an opportunity for deep bonding, and reflection in a retreat setting.

Members of Sunflower House have considerable less rhythmic body movement in their experiences than is common in public workshops. They have more abuse, death, and surrender experiences. They seem to be more psychic, having easier access to the rich symbolism of the unconscious. They seem better able and more eager than the average participant to depict (through drawing their mandalas) and articulate aloud (in the Sharing Group) their non-ordinary states of consciousness experiences.

It is still not clear which addicts in recovery should do Breathwork and in what stage of recovery they should do it. It seems to us that some members have had difficulty with 'bad' experiences in the Breathwork (e.g., reliving guilt too much, too soon); some have had trouble with 'good' experiences which seem in too great a contrast with their negative self-image in ordinary reality and ordinary desperate circumstances. Members who relive incest may need additional incest survivor support and information. Staff should be alert to relapse behavior, especially in the two weeks immediately following a Breathwork session.

There are some differences in the life experiences and in the Breathwork experiences of the men and women members, though there is not too much difference in their choices of drugs or the length of time they used the drugs. Women experience more sadness, less positive memories, less positive feelings about themselves. Men experience more anger, more positive feelings, and more often relive serious accidents or near death experiences. Women who have breathed are much more likely to use groups to talk about their experiences in Breathwork and have a slightly higher success rate with sobriety than the men who have breathed.

In this high risk population we need to stress certain precautions to prevent the spread of contagious diseases and to avoid risk to members with a long, untreated history of high blood pressure.

Implementation of Holotropic Breathwork works best when administration and staff have personally experienced a Breathwork session and are in full support of Breathwork as an adjunct to treatment of addicts in recovery.

Update—January 1994 by Kylea Taylor

When Steve Macy and I presented our paper on the use of Holotropic Breathwork at the Therapeutic Community of Sunflower

House in Santa Cruz, at the Association for Holotropic Breathwork International Conference in May 1993, we reviewed participants to determine their substance abusing status. In the 18 months since we had begun doing Breathwork, 56 participants had participated. Of those, we made a conservative estimate that 55% were still clean and sober and had remained free of court-involvement. Some additional others had minimal court involvement or had relapsed briefly. The rest either were using substances or had returned to jail or prison or their status was unknown. Since Sunflower House is often the treatment of last resort for long-term drug users and alcoholics, we considered this 55% to be a positive, though preliminary, statistic. We also noted that 44% of the few who filled out a final questionnaire said they had had a life-changing insight during a Breathwork session.

The Holotropic Breathwork has continued to be a periodic part of the treatment offered at Sunflower House. I changed the pre-questionnaire to incorporate a checklist of experiences which participants had had. We have continued to collect this data on the 'pre-session' forms as well as data from the *Same-Day Post-Questionnaires*. We do not have consistent data from the *Two-Week Post-Questionnaire,* and I have given up trying to administer the *Final Post-Questionnaire* entirely for now. The data I have gathered since May 1993 has languished in my files for want of time and money to process it.

In July 1993, funding was curtailed and I, as a part-time staff member, was laid off. The staff believes that Holotropic Breathwork is such a valuable adjunct to treatment that money was allocated for me to come back as a consultant to hold Breathwork sessions once every two months. I decided to volunteer to lead a follow-up group two nights after the Breathwork sessions as an experiment. In that group we checked-in and worked with feelings, the experiences they had, and the images from the drawings they have done after the sessions. This follow-up group has been very well received. I feel that it gives participants a chance to share and make some sense of the deep feelings (grief, existential dilemmas, and fear) which may have been stirred up in the session.

As part of my consultancy I began doing 'live' instead of videotaped introductions to the work. This enabled me to make a more direct response to their individual concerns about Breathwork and to screen participants more completely for contraindications.

Members do not usually do the Breathwork until they have been in the program at least a month. Participation is still voluntary. Those who volunteer are screened by the staff for their ability to make use of the process at their individual stage in treatment.

During the time since May 1993, I think I may have also solved the mystery of why the participants in this program did not move much physically during the sessions. I started talking about how, during their drug use, they had had to 'watch their backs' while in non-ordinary states of consciousness. It was a question of habit and a question of trust. I talked a lot about trusting their own inner wisdom (instead of focusing on whether or not to trust the facilitator), and I also added a time during the initial relaxation when they could contact their source of inspiration such as their Higher Power and therefore begin to allow the unfolding of the experience which would be appropriate for them today. The participants began moving in the same ways people do in the public workshops!

We have not had any other (besides the two residents I talked about in the paper) leave because of a too intense (and not integrated) Breathwork session. Staff has been very supportive of residents following the session.

The final difference is that staff, including the program manager, has begun to breathe along with the members, role-modeling surrender, risk, vulnerability, and continuing personal growth.

Postscript—2006 by Kylea Taylor

During the years from 1993 to 1999 in which I continued to facilitate Breathwork at Sunflower House, all of us who served on staff, particularly the program director, Kelly Sims Dovas, the program manager, Steve Macy, and I became more attuned to what was needed before and after the Breathwork session.

Prevention of relapse behavior after Breathwork

We learned to remove whatever load of responsibilities the participant was carrying in the TC community by having them delegate it completely during the two days of the breathwork process. This often proved to relieve stress and allow the participant to truly immerse him or herself in the experience of breathing or sitting.

We began to generate a participant list a week ahead of time and encourage those participants to "drop guilt" in group before they participated in Holotropic Breathwork. This is a process similar to the one that the Huichol Indians go through in community before taking peyote ritually together, and the practice worked well for the TC community also. We found that when a member had prepared and had done the difficult task of "coming clean" before Breathwork, that the Breathwork experiences would be more profound and there would be less relapse behavior afterward. Part of the psychology that worked may have been that participants felt deserving of the experiences they had in Breathwork and felt more ownership of these experiences, because they had invested themselves by way of difficult preparation.

Follow-up to and integration of Breathwork experiences

We found that the ideal time to hold a follow-up group was two days after the Breathwork sessions. We discovered the best way to do it was to have separate women's and men's groups. The half of the members who had supported the Breathwork by cooking and silence in the house would also go to these groups, men with men, women with women. Each person in the group would have a chance to share what the Breathwork had been like for them, whether they had been a participant or a supporter. We found this an excellent way to integrate the Breathwork people back into the larger residential community. The women were much more likely to talk about such things as memories of abuse in the all-female group than they had been when we had a follow-up group of both male and female Breathwork group participants.

It is my belief now that residents who left the program after doing Breathwork, in the early period in which we did Breathwork at Sunflower House, did not have the support to help them with the onslaught of shame which sometimes happened after a Breathwork session. Many participants had experienced much shaming along with abuse in childhood. In the later period in which we did Breathwork at this TC, we had structures in place for support of all the residents in the program following the intense days of Breathwork. As a staff we were much more aware of the signals of participants requiring more TLC and attention, and we were more skilled at providing the integration necessary between the non-ordinary state of consciousness experience and the ordinary life and behavioral therapy of the treatment program.

Unfortunately, Sunflower House is no longer a Therapeutic Community. Due to funding cuts, the name and the type of the program housed there has changed. The residential program is now 30-60 days instead of its previous year or more of treatment, and the program is focused on breaking down denial in the first stage of recovery. Holotropic Breathwork is no longer a part of the program. I hope that someone will be able to use what we learned at Sunflower House to provide the resource of Holotropic Breathwork to addicts in recovery. The research questionnaires developed for and used in this program are available for others to use for further research.

~5~

SoulCollage*
An Art Process to Use
with Breathwork

[First published in 2002 in The Healing Breath *online journal and* The Inner Door, *14(3)1, 4-5 and republished 2003 in Taylor, [Ed.] 2003,* Exploring Holotropic Breathwork. *Edited 2006.]*

SoulCollage is the process of making a deck of cards, one card at a time, using collage to depict one experience or one kind of energy per card. Many pieces of collage art are rather large and have a multiplicity of messages and images. SoulCollage cards often are more simple. Each five inch by eight inch card in one's growing deck of cards represents a facet of oneself (*e.g.*, a sub-personality, a community figure, an energy, or an archetype), which one finds relevant to and operant in one's life. Or, a card can depict an experience (dream or journey) such as a Breathwork journey. Author of the book, *SoulCollage,* and developer of the process, Seena B. Frost, says that, "the whole deck reflects the panorama which is *you* — your SoulCollage."

SoulCollage, like Breathwork, facilitates connection with self, connection with others, and artistic self-expression, which is a way to make both internal and external connection. SoulCollage provides a means for connection and self-expression immediately following the session. This continues as people go on to make, reflect on, and use, and share their cards.

After my first SoulCollage success, with six post-breathers happily collaging at my dining room table after their weekend breathwork workshop, I introduced it at two other Holotropic Breathwork events in 2001. One was *Trauma and Transformation*, a six-day training module of the Grof Transpersonal Training (GTT) held in Sedona, AZ, USA. The other was the two-week *Certification Intensive*, which concludes GTT's nine-week, residential training requirements. It was held in Taos Ski Valley, NM, USA. Some of the personal quotes that follow in this article are from participants who attended those two Holotropic Breathwork trainings.[1]

Holotropic Breathwork has always included art

Holotropic Breathwork has always included an art component in its technique. The Grofs, developers of Holotropic Breathwork, both brought art into the structure of the work. Christina Grof had worked as an art teacher. Her own art had facilitated and illustrated her personal spiritual emergence and recovery from post-traumatic stress. Stan Grof had used Joan Kellogg's technique of 'mandala' drawing effectively as part of the research protocol for the therapeutic use of psychedelics in his early work at the Maryland Psychiatric Research Institute in Baltimore, Maryland. From these separate streams, the Grofs had incorporated their own synthesis of 'mandala' art into Holotropic Breathwork.

The mandala art of Holotropic Breathwork

At the end of a Holotropic Breathwork session, participants usually are presented with a large circle penciled onto a sheet of paper from a large sketch pad. Breathers are encouraged to take the opportunity to express themselves in this non-verbal, but concrete way, even before the verbal sharing. It is a step towards integrating the intangible, non-ordinary experience of Breathwork with tangible, ordinary life. Often participants draw something that will remind them of the experiential events of their session. Sometimes what they draw is mysterious. Its meaning, immediately after the session, is as yet unclear. These 'mandalas', as we call them are usually descriptive of the process just experienced, but occasionally seem to be predictive of an unfolding process through which more will be revealed at a later time. Sometimes the mandala tells a story. Sometimes it simply expresses emotion by the placement and intensity of colors.

What is SoulCollage?

SoulCollage is an expressive art process—the process of making a deck of cards, one card at a time, using collage to depict one experience or one kind of energy per card. Many pieces of collage art are rather large and have multiple messages and images. SoulCollage cards are usually more simple.

SoulCollage and the therapeutic objectives of Breathwork

High on the list of therapeutic benefits of Breathwork are connection to self and others and increased trust in one's own creativity and self-expression. The deeper and more effective breathing and the setting induces a non-ordinary state of consciousness, which enables one to reconnect with parts of oneself from which one has become disconnected. Because Holotropic Breathwork is done mainly in groups, there is also a benefit of reconnection, even sometimes reconciliation, between individuals and groups. Participants experience deep process side by side with strangers and experience the common thread of humanity through entering the deep well of spirit together. People who know each other before doing Breathwork together deepen their relationships too. People who come from different ethnic or cultural backgrounds often find that greater respect and understanding replaces their preconceived and alienating beliefs about differences.

91

SoulCollage also makes internal and external connection easier, facilitating connection with self, connection with others, and connection with images in artistic self-expression. SoulCollage provides a means for connection and self-expression immediately following the session, and continues to do so as people go on to make more cards and reflect on them, use the cards for personal readings, and share their deck with others.

Maria feels that Breathwork and SoulCollage "complement each other as techniques of self-discovery."

> *After a Breathwork session, doing artwork such as SoulCollage helps to center oneself, to ground and have more clarity over the experience, have a better sense of one's feelings—something about our hands bringing form out of the inner to the outer world. SoulCollage helps in the integration of a Holotropic Breathwork session.*

Connection with one's own experience and self

Arnold theorizes that the inner healer[2] might more easily use collage as an art process in healing work:

> *SoulCollage is immediately rewarding because one can select/work with pictures that one is not able to draw. This opens up new inner material and relationships to be expressed. I feel that the 'resonance' one experiences when tearing out and working with a picture is an important healing signal from one's inner healer. This contrasts the confusion and uncertainty that a wounded person normally feels.*

Jeff was surprised to find, in a synchronistic way, images which perfectly expressed his process:

I had a session that involved raging against the unjust use of force, especially by uniformed people against unarmed folks (especially minorities). I was amazed as I ran through a couple magazines how many pictures seemed relevant. This tended to intensify and somehow affirm that the archetype I encountered is really present. Then arranging the images around a central figure that I drew added to this feeling of having touched on a 'real' issue. I've not done any sandbox[3] work, but there was a 'concrete' quality to even the use of the images that added power to the artwork part of my integration. Also I find that the collage 'locks in' the energy and feeling of the session in a way that my other art hasn't, when I later want to review it.

Images bypass the mind to select *you*

Unlike decks of cards (Tarot and others) that one can buy ready-made to use for readings, the SoulCollage cards contain the personal images *you* select—or, more accurately, the images that select *you*—coming straight through your Soul, bypassing the mind. Author Frost says that the process is a somewhat mysterious one:

You may or may not know what the image you select means at first. You may not know how you will use it and even if you will. What you feel is a power in this particular one. As you leaf through magazines, something stops and holds you, calls to you in a mysterious way. Something goes straight into your soul, bypassing the mind. Something vital in the image stirs you, and your imagination becomes engaged. You tear it out and save it!

SoulCollage cards assist in amplification of Breathwork experiences

Holotropic Breathwork facilitators are trained never to analyze someone's experience, but to assist in amplifying that experience by increasing awareness, or suggesting resources through which a participant may discover more facets of the experience and find personal meaning from them. SoulCollage assists with this. For example, Arnold reports:

> SoulCollage has amplified my Breathwork process. For example, I start with a picture of myself as a young child whom I experience often in my breathing sessions. As the collage develops, I find myself including pictures of trains, which I loved as a child; and also pictures of other favorite activities such as playing in the sand and swimming. The resulting collage consists of my happy childhood interests that I had forgotten about, but were elicited by the SoulCollage process after a breathing session.

Jeff, who was certified at the two-week intensive found that,

> SoulCollage is as (or more) effective as mandala drawing, for me. I find that selecting images (and just going through a lot of them to pick what has charge) is a very evocative process in itself. It definitely helps 'draw out' the core feelings from my session.

SoulCollage cards may help integrate Breathwork experiences

During the *Trauma and Transformation* module, participants depicted both trauma and transformation on their SoulCollage cards. Arnold describes his process:

> The ability of the SoulCollage to express and help integrate opposites within my psyche. A collage can show pictures of strong animals versus weak animals; or loving people versus killing people. The collage provides a safe container for the expression of conflicting, conscious/unconscious energies within myself. The collage is like a snapshot of a whole gestalt or of a COEX[4] in one's Unconscious. Looking at a

collage over time helps me assimilate and gives me a new perspective on previously separated parts of myself.

In the final session of a group, the cards provide a focus for individual closure and give a tangible art piece for each to take home from the sessions' experiences. The non-ordinary experience is validated and honored by a creation, which can even be used again and again to contact that personality part or archetypal energy. The final sharing group of the *Trauma and Transformation* module was quite moving as participants passed their stunning cards around the group. Claire wrote about that final sharing,

> *I saw the power of the cards when everyone shared their mandalas or SoulCollage cards. The expressiveness and creativity I saw on the cards made me realize just how powerful SoulCollage is and especially after a Breathwork.*

Using the SoulCollage Cards in an on-going way

Claire described her enjoyment in having the SoulCollage cards as an on-going project during the module:

> *The way it was set up in the module I attended was perfect, because I could go back and work on my cards at different times of the day and on different days. I did not feel pressured to finish. This would be more difficult in a one-day workshop setting due to the time constraints. I would still want to offer it and perhaps let people take cards home to work on.*

The process can continue in an on-going way after a workshop as well. The mat board collage cards are easy to make, keep, transport, and use. They can be easily ordered as pre-cut blank cards at www.soulcollage.com. People cherish their cards and delight in sharing them with family, friends, or in groups. They are a lovely and tangible reminder of an important experience.

For some the cards become allies on their own paths. In drawing the SoulCollage cards from their deck in a ceremonial way, they find the cards 'speaking' to them about the on-going questions of life. This is one way to remember to listen to guidance from different parts of themselves at crucial times. The book gives examples of how to use SoulCollage cards in this divinatory or therapeutic way, both in groups and individually.

Claire suggests that the SoulCollage process may continue the integration process well after a Breathwork session is finished. Integration is the process of bringing more of one's unconscious material to consciousness and into skillful use in ordinary life and relationship. Reclaiming a memory, a disowned emotion, or finding new personal meaning from fitting together things that had formerly been kept separately.

> *Two days after one of my recent Breathwork sessions, I took a magazine I had and saw some pictures that perfectly illustrated what I was feeling around the Breathwork. I felt driven and made three cards out of those pictures. They express so well what I had been feeling inside for years and could not put into words.*

Author Frost describes the divinatory process with SoulCollage:

> When we draw SoulCollage cards from our deck and lay them out to consult, it is like singing over our own dry bones. The cards represent all the many parts of ourselves, the happy and the sad, the wise and the foolish, the large and the small. When we lay them out and sing over them they come to life and reveal to us the wisdom for which we yearn.

Communion in doing collage work side by side

Although a mandala drawing room is usually quiet after Holotropic Breathwork, there seems to be a different quality of mood in a room when people are engaged in the SoulCollage process. Arnold, who was present at both residential modules when we used the process, noted that same quality as I had when we did the first SoulCollage/Breathwork experiment at my home-based workshop. He says:

> *The conscious intent of Breathwork participants making their SoulCollages affected me. Everyone seemed to be present and deeply focused in the work. A deep, meditative field seemed to be encompassing everyone, yet everyone was having fun. I felt welcomed and I wanted to join in.*

Peggy has a touching story about bonding with another participant in the 'mandala room' while doing her SoulCollage work:

> *I sat across the table from a man who was diligently working (upside down from my vantage point) on a mandala collage into the early hours of the morning. We said nothing. We were two of only three people in the room for hours on end. The only interaction we had was to pass the paper cement back and forth. I watched as he constructed his strikingly graphic image—a cross, filled with diverse people's faces on the background of a blue sky filled with clouds in a mandala circle.*
>
> *Early on, I hated what I was doing, but having been in this same place many times before, I continued trying to hold the words that came to me while doing the bodywork after the Breathwork session: "Love me, kill me." I was envious of the man across the table from me. His image was better than mine! Old stuff coming up again. Watching, watching—listening to the inner voices of criticism—continuing to meticulously cut out images that drew me to them. Then the pasting... That's when it all started to come together for me. The background that I had done with vivid primary colors: red, black, yellow, blue was the perfect receptacle for the images I had cut out. Finally, the man got up without saying anything and walked toward the door. I hadn't seen what he had ended up with. I ran after him. "May I see what you've done?" These were the first words*

we had said to each other. He proudly showed me his finished mandala. "It's incredible. How wonderful." I could see in his face that he was not only pleased with his own work, but pleased that I appreciated it as well. I no long felt any envy, just pride in what he had done—I felt as if I had somehow participated in his work. He asked to see what I was still in process on and commented on the intensity of the work I had done earlier on when I was laying down the pastel crayon color and blending it into the paper. I hadn't noticed, but I knew he was right. I felt as if I was doing something that had great force and energy in it. No woozy pastels or color with the paper showing through for this image! And I also realized when I started to like what I was doing, I also felt no envy of the image work he was doing.

We said "Goodnight" and from then on, we who had not spoken to each other up to that point, greeted each other daily, danced together on the night before closing and said "Goodbye" as intimates. I felt our collage work 'together' bonded us to each other in a way that didn't happen for me with anyone else other than my sitting/breathing partner.

Nonverbal people can communicate deep personal meaning to others

Many nonverbal people or people who have something very difficult to say, such as those who have just had a Breathwork experience, find that the cards enable them to communicate in an authentic, satisfying way—first with images, the language of symbols, dreams, and archetypes, and then, after that opening, with words.

Even 'non-artists' can create satisfying art

Self-exploration is usually a lonely process with not many ways of connecting with others. Art or poetry have been traditionally ways in which a few skilled people have been able to bridge that isolation and share at levels below the reach of ordinary conversation.

SoulCollage seems to help achieve a communication with others that is not possible for most of us to do using other artistic media. Even if people find words adequate to describe their non-ordinary state experiences, the art done by others can help in understanding them. Kip said, "Seeing the work of others was inspiring as is the sharing of the mandalas. The visual always seems to add another dimension to the words people use to try to describe their work."

The special advantage of SoulCollage is that it requires no skill in art, yet allows those people with ordinary abilities to express their deepest personal meaning in a way that others can appreciate. By choosing and merging images which resonate at the deepest level, the ordinary person can create an artistic expression which also connects him or her to others who are conscious at that level.

Maria describes her experience overcoming frustration at not being able to represent by drawing alone what she felt during her Breathwork experience:

> It helped me to gather my psychic energy after the Holotropic Breathwork session; to recognize and accept the depth of the process experienced, and to represent the highlights of the session through the images chosen. I always enjoy Stan Grof's suggestion of drawing mandalas after Holotropic Breathwork sessions, yet I sometimes feel frustrated for being unable to draw what I envision. The SoulCollage is a good option for those moments, at times easier, it is fun how I pick the images, cut and glue, and I am surprised by what shows up on the card afterwards.

Seeing the SoulCollage cards of others deepens one's own experiences

The cards are filled with images that resonate with people's most inner experiences, and so it is common that the cards of other breathers can affect one at the deepest level. Maria said, *I felt affected by other people's SoulCollage* [cards] *through the effect of Oneness; One Soul, many collages.* Jeff found that his experiences of viewing another participant's cards before his own breathing session triggered emotions that had been deeply buried and thus contributed to his Breathwork experience.

> *I was definitely affected* [by her cards]. *It was very surprising and suddenly overwhelming to see many of her images spread out in the center of our space, and move amongst them.... My breathing session the day after I encountered* [her] *SoulCollage cards was filled with rage.... So it definitely facilitated my process!*

Would Holotropic Breathwork trainees and participants use SoulCollage in their own groups?

Many participants in the *Trauma and Transformation* module felt SoulCollage was an important part of that module. Patricia Meadows subsequently wrote about the process in *The Inner Door*[5]

Many participants seemed deeply immersed in the SoulCollage process throughout the week (not only after their Breathwork sessions) and highly praised this creative process. One participant expressed: *I was absorbed in the collage technique. I would like to suggest that... this collage technique be offered as part of all modules ...*

Others in the GTT Certification Intensive agreed that SoulCollage is a great addition to Breathwork. Jeff will "definitely make it an option in workshops I conduct in the future." He says that he wants to work with the process, however, without having a set agenda of trying to collect images that seem to fit.

> *I find those* [images] *that have charge and stay open to maybe, or not necessarily, completing the collage during the course of the day (or weekend, etc.) But to stay open to the collage letting me know when it is ready to be finished.*

Arnold writes also that the collage sets its own pace:

> *I would include SoulCollage as an optional integration tool in any Breathwork workshop I give, because it can appeal to people who cannot draw well. I would state to the group that the process may be time-consuming. There may not be enough time during the workshop to complete a card. I definitely would provide magazines, and I would give the general background and instructions for constructing a collage. I would emphasize that no one is under pressure to complete a collage at the workshop. If one makes a collage, it should be done at one's own pace.*

The consensus seems to be that SoulCollage should be offered as an option, but that nothing should be forced. One common suggestion was that there be plenty of time allowed for work on SoulCollage projects. Claire said, "[SoulCollage] seemed to bring out things from the Breathwork that were there, but not well defined. The only difficulty is that there generally is not enough time in a one-day Breathwork setting to do the cards." Some suggested that one should offer the opportunity to make either cards or large collages. Peggy and Kip both suggested that participants be encouraged to use mixed media, such as collage and drawing to represent the inner landscape in the best possible way at the time. Peggy wrote, "I was able to create something of great value to me by the combination of the two techniques." Kip envisions that SoulCollage *could be of use in other experiential workshops that would incorporate movement, meditation, and such.*

---

[1] I use the quotes and the names with the participants' permission.

[2] "The inner healer" is a term used in Holotropic Breathwork and could be understood as "Higher Power," "Spirit," "Inner Wisdom," or "Creative Force."

[3] This is a reference to Dora Kalff'ssandplay therapy which is based on Jungian concepts.

[4] COEX is the acronym for Grof's theory of "Condensed System of Experiences." These are experiences which are related by emotion and/or body sensation and grouped together, even though they may be a grouping that includes biographical, perinatal, and transpersonal types of experiences. More can be found about this in Grof's book, *Beyond the Brain* (1985), published by SUNY Press.

[5] Her article was later re-published in Taylor, K. [Ed.] (2003.) *Exploring Holotropic Breathwork*. Hanford Mead Publishers.

~6~

Spiritual Emergency and Trauma-Based Dissociative Disorders
Similarities in Description and Treatment

[First published in Spiritual Emergence Network Newsletter *(Fall 1993) and edited in 2007]*

Dissociation is a survival response to stress. At one end of the spectrum, dissociation is common in all of us. In the DSM IV, Dissociative Identity Disorder (DID)[1] is at the far other end of the spectrum of dissociation, and is therefore the clearest example of the dissociative mechanism. A child, in response to severe physical, emotional, and sexual abuse, separates her experience into manageable bits. She stores feelings and memories, too overwhelming to be carried in one consciousness, into separate cells of consciousness.

These separate parts share one body, but many of them develop unique identities (including gender, race, medical histories, age) which are different from the identities of the "host" alter personality, the one which does most of the daily functioning. These parts, called alters, can even be 'non-human', representing any of the transpersonal aspects with which humans are known to identify in states of non-

103

ordinary consciousness (e.g., animals, spirits, elements, archetypes.) (Ross, 1993)[2] (Holmes, 1993.) These alters may have varying degrees of relationship or co-consciousness with the other parts, or may have no relationship or no knowledge of the other parts. Many multiples do not even know they are multiple. The may have received other diagnoses if they have been in therapy, or they may have learned how to handle the multiplicity so that they carry on a life that looks no different to the outside onlooker from a life without stark divisions between states. Sometimes the 'host' or another alter even dominates the consciousness and the body for many years, so that there is no way for anyone to know about the multiplicity.

The treatment of DID

Until recently, most of the treatment of DID was done by psychiatrists. Psychiatry, using a medical model, confused Multiple Personality Disorder (MPD), later DID, with Schizophrenia, termed the syndrome a "Disorder," and sought (without consulting a multiple's internal system itself) to integrate the alters into the "host" personality, or to force the expulsion of unwanted alters, or both. There was minimal honor accorded to the integrity and autonomy of the multiple's system, and not much recognition of the extraordinarily creative, dissociative skills which a multiple has developed under severe threat to her survival. There was also little attempt to utilize the multiple's considerable skills with non-ordinary states in order to heal the dysfunctional areas of her life.

On the leading edge of traditional psychotherapy, those diagnosed with DID are being treated more often these days in an outpatient setting by therapists who are not physicians. A trauma-based treatment model acknowledges that the client is not to blame, is telling her truth, has experienced real pain, and can heal, as others have, from similar trauma.

One team of healers (Doris Bryant, Judy Kessler, and Lynda Shirar), which included two marriage, family, and child therapists and their former DID client, have written a wonderful book called *The Family Inside: Working with the Multiple*. They have made a considerable contribution to demystifying DID treatment and describing their own therapeutic process. Using a gestalt approach to the inner family system, the authors build relationships among the alters, as well as between the therapists and the multiple's internal and external systems. The therapists stress the principle of following the multiple's lead in treatment. They listen to each alter. They honor the system's resistance and sense of timing. They allow adequate time for each to find a way to belong to the system in a positive way.

On the leading edge of transpersonal psychotherapy, Holotropic Breathwork practitioners are also working with multiples. The multiples find that Holotropic Breathwork, as an adjunct to therapy, can provide a bridge between dissociation and consciousness. In her own words, one multiple expresses it this way:

> While the altered state experience felt familiar and similar to dissociating, and therefore a familiar and comfortable experience, it had a curiously different and almost paradoxical effect. It both allowed a 'buffered distance' from 'body-feeling reality' and an intense, but oddly 'safe' engagement with my body-feeling states...I have control over the extent of the experience as I modulate the

breathing...the Holotropic Breathwork container provides a 'safe place and way of being' which make the experience of the 'unsafe' possible. (Miller, 1993.)

Similarities between Spiritual Emergency and DID

It is interesting that the description of the multiple's second stage of treatment (retrieving memories and feelings) in *The Family Within* sounds very similar to the experience of someone in the turmoil of spiritual emergency. The author writes:

> *A very functional multiple may be less functional as she begins to have feelings and memories that are extremely disturbing...throwing the whole system into a state of confusion and fear. The experience of remembering is loss of control in the extreme. (Bryant, et. al. 154.)*

The authors also list other symptoms which can arise during this state, such as the heightening of manic behavior, depression, anxiety, suicidal thoughts, isolation, and shame. All of these are also common during periods of spiritual emergency. In both trauma-recovery and spiritual emergency we experience loss of our belief systems, our worldviews. We discover 'it is not the way we think it is'. Such loss involves our painful awakening from our previous state of dissociation from the truth. We often find we are not who we thought we were. In order to reclaim consciousness and secure a successful passage through both trauma-recovery and spiritual emergency, we require some of the same elements for healing: (1) an other's therapeutic presence, (2) psycho-education (set), and (3) a safe setting. We need a caring person(s) who will follow and support where our process leads us, we need maps for and understanding of the journey we are on, and we need a safe container in which to experience the fearsome unknown.

DID and spiritual emergency are also alike in that both include experiences with non-ordinary consciousness, transpersonal phenomena, and the functioning of the psyche in non-ordinary ways. The multiple develops a high degree of skill in autohypnosis, separates herself from ordinary reality, experiences identity with other life forms and spirits, travels outside the body, and often has "helping spirits." (Ross 1993) (Holmes 1993) (Miller 1993.) The person in the midst of spiritual emergency has these same experiences, especially in the psychic opening or shamanic type of spiritual emergency (Grof and Grof 1990.)

Miller (1993) has noted that a multiple's "attempts to conform to the exigencies of the hylotropic (ordinary conscious state) while unknowingly using the holotropic (non-ordinary consciousness) results in a system in which balance is fragile..." This sounds very much like Stanislav Grof's description of spiritual emergency as that area where ordinary reality and non-ordinary reality overlap and thereby create turbulence and confusion.

One final similarity between spiritual emergency and DID is that both are heroes' journeys; both send gifts through the individual's experience to the larger community of human beings. Both the people who complete the spiritual emergency and those who resolve their healing crisis as multiples often have more energy, creativity, compassion, and understanding to offer others. Their experiences also have many implications for the study of the healthy or highly functioning human psyche.

---

[1] The term, Multiple Personality Disorder (MPD), was updated to Dissociative Identity Disorder (DID) to conform to the Diagnostic and Statistical Manual's (DSM) current version, DSM-IV.

[2] Colin Ross, M.D. and Kathryn Steele, well known lecturers on the treatment of DID, presented at the 1993 Advanced Training on Multiplicity held by the Grof Transpersonal Training for certified Holotropic Breathwork facilitators. Stanislav and Christina Grof were also present for discussions. The sessions were audiotaped by Sounds True Recording.

~7~

Sponsoring
"Unexperienced Experience"

The term "sponsor" is one of those particularly apt names that really fits what Stanislav Grof has taught and modeled and which he and his wife, Christina, structured into the ritual of Holotropic Breathwork. The term "sponsor" in the 12-Step communities means one who has traveled somewhat further down a recovery road and who gives assistance to someone else traveling their own individual, but similar road. The term "to sponsor" is also used in Stephen Gilligan's Self-Relations theory, which he has written about in *The Courage to Love*. In Self-Relations theory, sponsoring is a way to describe a similar kind of assistance that is provided in the psychological context of professional therapy. Gilligan lists sponsorship skills as "deep listening, proper naming, providing a place, expressing, blessing, connecting, disciplining, protecting, encouraging, and challenging."[1]

In Holotropic Breathwork what I am calling "sponsorship" includes assisting the inner healer of someone in a non-ordinary state of consciousness and helping them express and amplify the energies and experiences which have not been welcomed and loved sufficiently in any previous context and therefore are actually "unexperienced experience" as Ivor Browne first termed them.[2] These unwelcomed energies emerging in holotropic process seem similar, when taken as a collective, to what have been called "the neglected self" by Gilligan.[3] One metaphor of the neglected self in Grof's teaching is a kind of a warehouse full of unexperienced experience. In this metaphor the inner healer moves with a flashlight through the dark storage room of the psyche.[4] The light finds the right piece of material that is ripe for healing in these circumstances provided at this time. In Holotropic Breathwork we sponsor by encouraging and supporting the whole emerging enactment of what wants now to emerge. In holotropic states (breathwork, hypnosis, psychedelic therapy, and shamanic work of various kinds), the neglected self of the psyche can include and take the form of:

- Archetypal energies that have not been allowed yet to express through the person

- Repressed memories (biographical, perinatal, or transpersonal)

- Repressed emotions (as above)

- Repressed physical sounds and movements

- Dissociated experiences or collections of experiences

- Dissociated knowing or cognitive understanding about events, feelings, or intuitions

- That part which has not felt worthy to be 'in relationship' or even to 'be here'

Our job as facilitators and sitters for the breather is to trust the breather's inner healer as it selects and processes such material, to witness what is coming forward, and, as appropriate, to encourage expression and integration of the material.

In Holotropic Breathwork the holotropic state often spontaneously includes a bi-modal consciousness comprised of both experiencing and witnessing. At the same time that one is deeply *in* the experience, one also usually has a witness present to this reliving of trauma, cosmic unity, or any other type of experience. The breather's sitter, by witnessing the breather's experience, also sponsors the inner witness of the breather by modeling (being an outer representation of) the witness function.

What comes forward in a Holotropic Breathwork session probably has been underground, since some point in time long ago, from lack of sponsorship. 'Positive' or 'negative', the perinatal or biographical experience didn't have enough support and resources (inner and outer) at the time something happened and therefore buried itself in the unconscious of the body/mind. Until the Breathwork session it may never have had another human presence and a ritual setting able to sponsor it. Transpersonal experiences, too, wait for proper conditions of sponsorship. Somehow the inner healer recognizes the supportive opportunity and selects or allows the material to come forward. At that point the task of a breather is to sponsor the awareness and the experiencing of the material so that it can ultimately be embodied and integrated. A breather or experiencer in non-ordinary states does her best to cooperate with the inner healer, to stay present with what is arising and to be *with* it (or *become* it) as fully as possible.

As a facilitator, or as a sitter, we also are cooperating with the person's inner healer as best we can, given our outside perspective on the unfolding process. A facilitator of Holotropic Breathwork offers "protection, permission and connection"[5] to the whole person in a holotropic state of consciousness and particularly to whatever part of person or his or her experience has been unconscious, denied, repressed, self-criticized. Sponsoring includes providing:

· *Protection* by creating a safe setting (enough time for the process to complete, freedom from interference, one-on-one care, confidentiality, ethical behavior, etc.)

111

- *Protection* through manifesting the fearless trust in the inner healer that is a result of many non-ordinary state experiences, both as an experiencer and as a sitter or facilitator, and of knowing the Grof Maps of Consciousness[6]

- *Permission* through providing information to the experiencer before the scheduled experience about the kinds of experiences possible in non-ordinary states of consciousness

- *Permission* through normalizing and encouraging expression that is already demonstrating what wants to occur

- *Permission* by empowering the unempowered self to make choices

- *Connection* through relationships between facilitator and breather, sitter and breather, inner healer and breather, and among all participants.

- *Connection* through compassionate touch, when appropriate for a corrective experience of early omission of nurturance

- *Connection* through providing resistant pressure to allow fuller experience and expression

One of the most useful maps for sponsoring deep experiences is the Grof Maps of Consciousness, particularly Grof's perinatal cartography. Joseph Campbell showed us the archetypal pattern of "The Hero's Journey," a cross-cultural myth representing the universal human experience of major passage and change. The hero receives the Call to Adventure, sets out across the Threshold, faces the Demons (the obstacles and trials of adversaries and adversities), and ultimately returns to his community and to a reconstituted wholeness in himself, bearing the wisdom and gifts he has received from his journey.[7] Stanislav Grof made this archetypal concept intensely personal by describing The Hero's Journey of each individual's birth passage from fetus to infant. He described the stages of birth and linked each to the very particular qualities and content of possible holotropic experiences.

I have found it useful many times in therapy sessions with clients to describe these birth stages. Briefly, there are four Basic Perinatal Matrices. (BPMs) or Birth Matrices.[8] Our birth experience in these stages seems to underlie other experiences we have in life as well as in non-ordinary states such as Holotropic Breathwork. Most of Grof's books describe these Matrices as does my book, *The Breathwork Experience*, so I will not repeat the full description of them here.

Briefly though, the First Matrix includes the period from conception until the onset of labor. The womb is the fetus' or embryo's universe and in a normal, unstressed pregnancy this may be a blissful time in which the fetus has its needs fulfilled. The Second Matrix starts when labor begins and sudden chemical and mechanical changes interrupt the normally peaceful, safe environment of womb. Strong contractions begin, trying to push the fetus down and out, but there is yet no exit to be found, because the cervix has not yet dilated to open the way for birth. In this painful stage, the fetus is stuck. This is the experience of feeling helpless and hopeless, stuck in the victim position. The Third Matrix begins when the cervix is sufficiently dilated to free the fetus to begin its passage down and through the birth canal. Metaphorically and actually, now there is light at the end of the tunnel. There is movement, and resolution suddenly seems possible, even if still difficult and not necessarily certain. There are powerful emotions: sexual feelings, aggression, anxiety, and often, particularly in a long labor, a period of intense struggle. The Fourth Matrix is birth itself, an experience, in the cutting of the umbilical cord and reconnection to the mother through nursing, of giving up the old to be born to something new.

These four Matrices are archetypal in quality and may lend their qualities to other non-ordinary state experiences. For example reliving a child abuse situation has the victim quality of the Second Matrix. The Second Matrix is the Matrix that most often needs sponsorship. It turns the comfortable 'womb' into a 'hell' with no exit.[9] It is the kind of experience both in birth and later in life which feels intolerable and overwhelming. It is the most likely kind of experience to be repressed, dissociated, or otherwise defended against. It is generally not experienced fully while it is happening, and no one wants to revisit it. The qualities of this stage of birth, or this type of later experience, are hopelessness, helplessness, betrayal, and timelessness. One feels that the suffering will never end and the inclination is to avoid it, not enter into it.

Sponsorship of people who are having a Second Matrix experience requires a 'both/and' approach. On the one hand, the only way through the suffering is to surrender to the timelessness of the experience and feel (suffer) whatever is emerging to be felt, whether it is a present time passage or an unexperienced experience from the past. The challenge for the facilitator (or therapist) and the experiencer is to enter this matrix of suffering without trying to fix it or end it. On the other hand, paradoxically, the Second Matrix is just one stage in a process, therefore it is not really timeless, and it will actually end. When a breather becomes aware of the larger map (the four Matrices taken as a whole) she understands that she is in a passage, that there will be an end to this part of suffering. She realizes that change is not only possible, but inevitable, despite her *feeling* that this experience is interminable and it would be hopeless to enter into it fully. To remember the Map is to remember that there is bigger worldview available than the particular viewpoint (depression and hopelessness) inherent in experiencing Second Matrix material. Remembering this larger picture makes surrender to the Second Matrix possible.

If the client is experiencing Third Matrix material, it is often useful to make a therapeutic prediction about the impulsive behavior that is likely to occur as someone wants to 'get it over with' and move to completion. This information might work to reduce risk-taking behavior, such as parachuting, for example. One would want to encourage the client to do the work on the inner, rather than outer, plane. I have found it helpful to discuss the Matrices with clients who are in fear of (or longing for) a change of identity, dying, facing loss of a loved one, or feeling actively suicidal.

As a therapist, although this is by no means my only tool, I tend to look at addiction and addiction recovery through the lens of the Matrices also[10]. I would try to assess from the problem symptom what neglected self the addict is trying to medicate and in which direction the addict is trying to go in the 'birth passage' to manage the symptom. Those who use opiates might be viewed as trying to move from the Second Matrix back to the First Matrix where they felt safer. Those who use amphetamines might be trying to speed up the process through the Third Matrix to get to the relief of the Fourth.

During the holotropic session, a facilitator encourages the breather to stay with it, really express (feel) it, breathe into it one more time, etc. Sponsorship may also include reminding a breather that the hell they are experiencing in the session has already happened long ago, and since they moved through it then, they can do so now. The intention is to do whatever it takes to help the breather fully own and embody the previously disconnected material. At the end of the session, the sponsoring facilitator and breather may begin to tune into a perspective *about* the experience, while at the same time being *in* the experience, together inquiring of the Mystery what needs to happen next to complete and integrate the material.

The essence of Grof's approach can be found in the word he coined, *holotropic*. Holotropic means *moving toward wholeness*.

Implicit in the word and its opposite motion, *hylotropic*, is that these processes of moving toward wholeness and moving toward separateness are in motion at every level, individual, cultural, and cosmic, and that the inner healer is a representation of that movement within the psyche. Work in non-ordinary states of consciousness is especially related to the holotropic motion of separate, disconnected parts moving toward wholeness once more.

Culturally we have dissociated, repressed, and otherwise defended against the healing potential of non-ordinary states of consciousness. Grof's writings have sponsored this neglected self in the collective psyche by creating a kind of therapeutic double bind. In his books he describes the extraordinary healing and the reports of his clients about their non-ordinary states. If psychology accepts that these strange, but healing, experiences do occur for human beings in holotropic states of consciousness, then the cultural doors of perception may open and the concept of the inner healer (and with it a whole cadre of perinatal and cosmic concepts) may just slip on through, conscious and ready to be utilized. In a computer metaphor, if you consider that "virus" maybe helpful in this case, if the concept of the inner healer has slipped past the outdated monoculture virus checkers, a paradigm shift has already installed itself in the operating system.

I remember the stunned feeling I often had while reading Grof's *Beyond the Brain* for the first time. That feeling was often followed by an almost Fourth Matrix sort of ecstasy at having transcended some cognitive lock. *Beyond the Brain* sponsors the most extraordinary human experiences while remaining in dialogue with the historical roots and more conventional current practice of western psychology and psychiatry. Grof takes a strong sponsorship position,[11] not only in asserting the reality of holotropic experiences, but also in naming and challenging the ignorance and fear with which the facts about holotropic experience have been met during the last centuries. Grof says, "The research of holotropic states of consciousness has important implications not only for each of us individually, but also for the future of humanity and survival of life on this planet."[12] Sponsoring the unexperienced experience of oneself and others is a contribution each of us can make to that future.

---

[1] Gilligan, S. (1997.) *The Courage to Love.* NY: W.W. Norton & Company. 97.

[2] Browne, I. (1990, Spring.) "Psychological Trauma or Unexperienced Experience." *ReVision.* 12, 21-33.

[3] Gilligan, S. (1997.) *The Courage to Love.* NY: W.W. Norton & Company. 144-145.

[4] Grof, S. (2000.) *Psychology of the Future.* Albany, NY: SUNY Press. 28-29.

[5] The term "protection, permission, and connection" were applied descriptively to the Grofs' work by Gould, Pacey, and Taylor in developing the Grof Transpersonal Training's *Trauma and Transformation* module. Taylor wrote about this concept also in "The Ritual of Holotropic Breathwork: The Healing Potential of Protection, Permission, and Connection for Trauma Recovery." (See page 119.)

[6] Grof addresses the need for a facilitator to have much experience personally and as a therapist working with non-ordinary states in order to be able to trust the process. He writes, "With the increase in the number of sessions that he or she has witnessed, the therapist becomes more comfortable with and less threatened by various unusual phenomena that are quite common in psychedelic [and other non-ordinary state] therapy. Witnessing positive resolution of such states and seeing the same subjects only a few hours later radiant and joking, the therapist gradually develops equanimity, confidence and tolerance in regard to the entire spectrum of psychedelic [and non-ordinary state] phenomena." Grof (1980. 107.)

[7] Campbell, J. (c1949, 1968.) *Hero with a Thousand Faces.* Princeton, NJ: Princeton University Press.

[8] Grof, S. (1980.) *LSD Psychotherapy.* 75-89 and Grof, S. (1985.) *Beyond the Brain.* 92-137.

[9] Grof, S. (1985.) *Beyond the Brain*. Albany, NY: State University of New York Press. 111.

[10] Riskin, T. (2000.) has come to a similar conclusion about the usefulness of the Matrices in therapy. He wrote an article in *The Inner Door*, "Using the Model of Perintal Matrices in Psychotherapy," and gives a number of case examples from his clinical practice. 59-60.

[11] In his later book, *Psychology of the Future*, Grof takes an even stronger position for the validity of non-ordinary experience and the need to include it in effective psychiatric practice, not only for individual healing, but for the survival of the human race.

[12] Grof, S. (2000.) *Psychology of the Future*. Albany, NY: SUNY Press. 293.

~8~

The Ritual of Holotropic Breathwork

The Healing Potential of Protection, Permission, and Connection for Trauma Recovery

[From a presentation given by Kylea Taylor at the 2004 International Transpersonal Association Conference in Palm Springs, California.]

When certain essential elements of recovery work are fully available and in balance, they act as allies for someone on the heroic journey of recovery from trauma and dissociation and help create an environment conducive to healing experiences. Holotropic Breathwork provides such a therapeutic container for corrective experiences in non-ordinary states of consciousness (NOSCs), and gives us a model for deep work of various kinds.

When I had completed the Grof Training and was doing my own workshops, I noticed that some of the aspects of Holotropic Breathwork had not been documented. These aspects had been well-covered in the training, but had not yet been written down.

I began to feel a calling to publish some of these aspects of Breathwork. There was no manual for facilitators, so I wrote one. I wrote my next book, *The Breathwork Experience*, because there wasn't any book that talked just about Breathwork. As I got deeper into the work, I saw that the non-ordinary states of consciousness (NOSCs) created ethical situations that were unique and much more complex than those in ordinary therapy and workshops. This led me to write *The Ethics of Caring* which explores those issues.

Lately, I've been interested in the role Holotropic Breathwork plays in trauma recovery. So, when Stan Grof asked me to present at this conference, I decided to begin to formalize my thinking about why Breathwork works so well in trauma recovery.

I realized that there were two elements of Holotropic Breathwork that I don't think have been too widely talked about.

These are the elements of community and of ritual, both of which are contained within the format of Holotropic Breathwork.

The role of Holotropic Breathwork in trauma recovery

What is trauma?

Post-Traumatic Stress Disorder (PTSD) is the Diagnostic and Statistical Manual (DSM IV) diagnosis for undigested experience, and for what Ivor Browne in 1990 called *un-experienced experience*.

Something is a too big, too painful, too shocking for one's physical or emotional or spiritual capacity at the time. It is too much for one's support system at the time, to validate and soothe. It is too dissonant an experience for one's belief system to assimilate or even contain. So we choose survival, and we enlist whatever defense mechanisms can help us—usually denial, repression, and dissociation. And thus, we survive.

120

We survive with the experience stored somewhere in a closed compartment of the psyche, where it waits for the right conjunction of conditions for its recovery. It is interesting that the word *recovery* means both *healing* and *finding and re-claiming*.[5]

Holotropic Breathwork is usually quite effective with PTSD

I've worked intensely over the years with many people in the Grof Transpersonal Training who were dealing with dissociation and recovering from trauma. I worked for nine years at a long-term residential addiction recovery center, running therapy groups three times a week and facilitating Holotropic Breathwork there every month or two. Some of my private therapy clients with PTSD also did Holotropic Breathwork in the workshops that Jim and I were facilitating monthly for 11 years. And many others with a history of trauma, who were not my therapy clients, were participants in these workshops as well.

We know that two of the major elements of Holotropic Breathwork are NOSCs and the concept of the *inner healer*. The elements of ritual and community are less frequently mentioned. Recently, I've been thinking that these elements—ritual and community—contribute in a major way, and perhaps are even essential to creating the synergy in this powerful method of healing.

I first started seriously looking at what contributes to Holotropic Breathwork's effectiveness with trauma recovery when two other women, Ingrid Pacey and Mary Louise Gould, and I were preparing a Trauma and Recovery Model for the Grof Transpersonal Training module, *Trauma and Transformation*.

In our three clinical practices in three corners of North America, we each had accumulated over 10 years of facilitating Holotropic Breathwork with trauma survivors. So together, the three of us sorted out three elements of process and structure that help trauma survivors in Holotropic Breathwork. We called these essential elements: *protection, permission,* and *connection*.

Other writers have found similar elements necessary to the structure and process of trauma recovery. For example, Babette Rothschild in her book, *The Body Remembers: The Psychophysiology of Trauma and Treatment*, wrote the "Ten Foundations for Safe Trauma Therapy."

The First Foundation says, "establish safety for the client." This is the role of *protection*. Rothchild's Second Foundation of Safe Trauma Therapy starts in this way… "develop good contact…" and her Fourth Foundation includes the statement, "identify and build on the client's internal and external resources." Both of these latter phrases are describing the role of *connection*.

Ritual in Holotropic Breathwork

I also started thinking about how Holotropic Breathwork is a ritual—and how cultures over the millennia have used ceremonies as healing processes.

In one large anthropological study, 90% of cultures studied had some form of ritual NOSCs that were sanctioned as essential parts of the main culture.[6]

In reading further about ritual, I was struck by the very simple idea that ritual seems to be used mostly to help people deal with the most formidable challenges with which humans have to come to terms.

Much ritual is about helping people deal with change. There are, of course, rituals and ceremonies for other purposes, but many, many of them have to do with helping us through life transitions—helping with birth, puberty, marriage, other changes in social status or identity, illness, or death.

Rituals not only help individuals deal with change; ceremonies also help the groups, systems, and cultures which support the individuals. The rituals help those systems absorb the changes. People need help with change because impermanence means grief and loss. Grief and loss accompany change, even so called 'positive' change. Many rituals are designed to help us close the curtain on one act and open the curtain to the next act. Trauma recovery is about change. Actually, recovery from trauma *is* change, and rituals, as I have said, are often designed to help with change.

We have tended, for the most part, to think about Holotropic Breathwork as a way to do individual process. Martin Boroson in 1998 wrote a wonderful article entitled, "Radar to the Infinite,"[1] which we re-published in the book, *Exploring Holotropic Breathwork*. This article helped Holotropic Breathwork facilitators realize that the very thing that made Holotropic Breathwork so difficult to explain to others—its very broad scope—was also its greatest asset. The asset is that, unlike most techniques that are directed towards some particular experiential outcome, Holotropic Breathwork welcomes any kind of experience that might arise for an individual in a NOSC. For example, Individuals could spontaneously assume yoga postures, do meditation, become shamanic allies, move wildly, relive birth, or dance beautifully, to name just a few types of diverse, available experiences.

Holotropic Breathwork is valuable for individuals, and individual process is important. For years, I thought about Holotropic Breathwork in that way—as a place for individual process. At the same time in a semi-conscious way, I knew that the primary personal reason that moved me to enroll in the Grof Transpersonal Training was that I was seeking a community—people who were interested in and who could support inner exploration and change for each other. What I have begun to realize is that there is a lot more to Holotropic Breathwork than individual process.

Holotropic Breathwork is a ritual

I have come to understand that the group work of Holotropic Breathwork is a ritual, and that Holotropic Breathwork offers the same benefits that ritual has offered to groups of individuals since the beginning of history. It incorporates important elements of ritual structure. These are general elements of ritual that have been named, described, and studied by anthropologists. I think these elements form a crucial, and often overlooked, part of the success of Holotropic Breathwork, particularly with trauma recovery.

Holotropic Breathwork has its roots in what has worked for humans for a long time. Stan and Christina Grof left those thick roots of ancient wisdom intact when they grafted on a simple ritual for modern times. Holotropic Breathwork has been pruned of culturally-specific symbols and dogma, so that it can work very well cross-culturally.

Holotropic Breathwork started with a rootstock that included: 1) the value of NOSCs; 2) the value of shared group experience; and 3) the concept of the 'inner healer'.

The value of non-ordinary states of consciousness (NOSCs)

In this mono-culture of modern times, we all share the taste memory of McDonald's French fries, but most of us don't have a shared cultural, centuries-old, ceremonial way of accessing NOSCs. The simple elements of breathing and music in Holotropic Breathwork allow diverse persons, even if they don't have shared symbols, to go on deep healing journeys, side by side.

The global village—the value of shared group experience

All across the earth now, small sections of our global village are convening for Holotropic Breathwork workshops to experience ritual together. At this time, there are nearly 900 certified facilitators of Holotropic Breathwork from at least 36 countries. Many are facilitating workshops in their own lands, in their own cultures, and in their own languages. Some of these global villagers even create on-going community together.

124

Certainly this happens at the Grof Transpersonal Training, where people reconvene in various formations together over the two or three years of the average person's training period, but also some facilitators hold regular workshops and build on-going community. Ken and Petra Sloan are examples of facilitators building community through their regular weekend workshops and weeklong Breathwork retreats in Germany.

Some people meet only for one-day workshops and then disband as a 'village', but they may be changed to some extent by participation even for one day in this modern ritual.

Rituals provide stability during profound periods of change. Rituals seem to provide a rope of tradition to cling to while crossing the turbulent river between two territories. On one side of this river is the territory of the known. On the other side is the territory of the new or unknown. The fact that the rope is even there is a signpost that gives notice. Someone has crossed here before. We can hold onto that meta-communication and onto more concrete structures for support.

The structure and cartography of Holotropic Breathwork provides a kind of rope to hold onto in the confusing turbulence of change. Holotropic Breathwork is designed to provide set and setting that makes it safe enough to experience new territory.

The ordeal of ritual

Rituals also often have an element of ordeal. Holotropic Breathwork is not an easy workshop commitment. A Holotropic Breathwork workshop is usually a very long day. It is also a commitment to surrender to an unknown experience. It requires travel, a lot of packing and schlepping of pillows and blankets, and a lot of focused awareness, both as a breather and a sitter. Not to mention that breathing faster and deeper is often hard work. It is not easy. Change often seems to require some sort of ordeal.

The stages of ritual

Ritual helps us with change in three stages. These three stages of ritual were named by anthropologist, Victor Turner, with the word, *liminal*, from the root *limen*, meaning a *threshold*. Ritual helps us with change also by creating a condition Turner called *communitas*.

The first stage of ritual

The first stage of ritual is the *pre-liminal* preparation stage, in which participants begin to remove themselves from ordinary reality and separate from former or ordinary social structure and constraints. In Holotropic Breathwork that stage begins with the decision to participate, and continues through what we often call The Introductory Talk.

The Introductory Talk

For many participants, The Introductory Talk is the first place they have encountered the outlandish (outside of current cultural instruction) ideas of transpersonal psychology. If they have encountered these ideas before, it may have been in the privacy of their own reading room. For some, at least, this is the very first place in which they have heard so many of these strange ideas all at once.

It is often the first place they have encountered a whole group of other people who have come with the same interest in venturing out of ordinary states of consciousness.

In the Introductory Talk, facilitators describe the Grof Cartography of the Psyche, which is a map of those experiences which tend to arise in NOSCs. Grof's expanded cartography offers protection and permission. This notifies the inner healer that any kind of healing experience will be welcome in the setting of Holotropic Breathwork.

Grof's perinatal map, the Basic Perinatal Matrices, or the Birth Matrices, offers help with the stages of birth, which are also the stages of any subsequent major life change. The Birth Matrices help give trauma survivors a sense of time. The Birth Matrices define a progression, a passage.

The value of the Birth Matrices to trauma survivors

The Matrices reassure that there is a beginning, a middle, and an end to process and change. Often, dissociated fragments of trauma memory feel timeless to survivors. When they are re-experiencing a trauma memory, it can feel like the hopeless, helpless, timeless state of the Second Matrix. They really do not know they will survive it. It feels like endless terror. Knowing and remembering that the Third and Fourth Matrices exist, that the process will end, and that they did indeed survive the experience when it first happened, may make the difference in someone being able to tolerate the 'intolerable' pain of reliving a trauma memory.

Grof's expanded cartography also helps make sense of kundalini, shamanic, and psychic phenomena. My own experience of kundalini, in its very active time with me, was that it was re-connecting my body and my consciousness—re-opening energy channels, feelings, and sexuality.

I have seen a lot of pranic phenomena and some kundalini phenomena in Breathwork participants. My impression is that those who are recovering from physical or sexual abuse often have many kinesthetic experiences in the process of reclaiming memory and sensation in their bodies.

Shamanic phenomena and other transpersonal experiences also occur frequently for survivors. One theory is that survivors may have easier access to the transpersonal realms, because they were forced to reach for that realm as a resource when there were no resources in ordinary life to aid them during the time of their abuse.

Trauma survivors often develop psychic resources because of their extreme need to maintain hypervigilance in order to keep out of harm's way. Hypervigilance seems to sharpen the sixth sense as well as the five other senses.

Holotropic Breathwork validates these transpersonal resources in the Introductory Talk—validates them as *real* experiences, even if they are non-ordinary experiences. These resources are often re-accessed and re-claimed during Breathwork. Many internal connections can be made between dissociated resources, archetypal energies, and other parts of the mind during Holotropic Breathwork.

One young man, in his 20s, at the drug treatment program, participated in Breathwork and got in touch with the truth that he had been abused in a prolonged and particularly horrific way during his childhood. This young man had never felt the *meaning* of what had happened to him, even though he had always remembered the *facts* of what had happened to him. He felt enough protection and permission from the combination of Breathwork, the staff, and the community in the residential setting to reconnect to this piece. After the Breathwork, he had a spiritual emergency for about a week while he was trying to absorb the truth and reality that he had been abused. He would come up to me and other staff members dozens of times each day to say. "I was abused. Kylea, I was abused!" He would be looking into our faces to help him believe what he was saying was true.

After the Introductory Talk, the final part of the pre-liminal preparation stage of ritual in Holotropic Breathwork is the physical business of setting up of blankets and pillows, putting on eyeshades, making agreements with sitters, and then, settling in to go through the threshold experience of the Guided Relaxation and beginning to breathe.

The second stage of ritual—the *liminal* stage

The second stage is what is commonly considered the ritual itself, the *liminal* stage. This stage includes NOSCs and a special set and setting, so that the ritual and people in it are set apart from ordinary reality.

128

Holotropic Breathwork is often done with two breathing sessions plus a sharing group. The day, as a whole, is set apart from ordinary reality as a day of retreat. The breathing, faster and deeper, is the catalyst for the NOSCs, which are quite set apart from ordinary states of consciousness.

Communitas

In the *liminal* state, ritual participants together create the kind of group relationship that Turner called *communitas*. I was delighted to discover a word for what I have seen happen over and over in a Holotropic Breathwork group. *Communitas* is a temporary relationship of intimate equals facing change together.

In Holotropic Breathwork people come together temporarily, in a sacred setting. They enter a NOSC at the same time. They are free to move and make sounds. They receive caring from others. They hear and share intimate experiences. If they breathe regularly together, a deep bond usually forms. They witness change for each other. There is support. Change itself becomes less frightening.

How does ritual provide *protection*?

Rituals provide security and structure by requiring traditional behaviors—proscribed, known, repetitive, and expected behaviors. Most of us human beings seem to need to keep one foot on ground that seems stable and familiar, while we launch the other toe (or more perhaps) into the ocean of change.

In Holotropic Breathwork, facilitators provide a standard model as an anchor: There is an Introductory Talk, a Breather/Sitter relationship, Music, Bodywork, Art, and a Sharing Group.

The sameness of the model each time allows us to relax with what is known and trusted, so that at the point of beginning to breathe, we can surrender to what will be unknown on the journey.

Protection and trauma survivors

Protection is particularly crucial for trauma survivors. One of the ways Holotropic Breathwork establishes safety is the one-on-one caring by the sitter. The sitter provides awareness and resources from the ordinary state of consciousness to the NOSC. Examples are handing a breather a tissue, giving her water, and steadying her on her trip to the bathroom.

Another way Holotropic Breathwork offers safety is that facilitators make contracts with participants about their participation—contracts about confidentiality, staying for the whole workshop, not hurting self, others, or property, and not acting out sexually with another person during the workshop. There is an *explicit* contract that the *participant* is in charge of whatever help or touch they want or don't want.

Control over one's own physical boundaries is essential to someone in trauma recovery. There is an implicit contract that the trained facilitators are going to provide support if someone gets into unknown territory.

A very significant factor in the quality of protection available in Holotropic Breathwork is the quality of training that facilitators have had. All certified facilitators have had at least 600 hours of training and supervision in not less than two years of the GTT curriculum. That includes equal amounts of experiential and didactic process in the broad transpersonal curriculum.

Most of us, when we were going through the training, found ourselves in a place or two where we were terrified, but then we had the experience of getting through the terror by facing it, embodying it, taking risks, and receiving support. We learned experientially, not just theoretically, to trust in the inner wisdom or the *inner healer*. Trust helps us be able to be there for participants, and to give them protection and permission when we are facilitating.

The *permission* available in ritual

In addition to *protection*, ritual also provides authorization—
theoretical, cultural, and group authorization, or *permission*. There
is sanction given, from actually-present human beings, to explore,
and even become or embody, the unknown and the mystery.

Holotropic Breathwork also offers permission with its concept of
the inner healer. The inner healer is that force that summons white
blood cells and immune function to heal a physical wound in the
body. The inner healer is that same innate wisdom that also
summons up appropriate psychic material when we go into NOSCs.
Stan Grof has bestowed on Holotropic Breathwork what Rick Tarnas
has termed, "Stan's 'radical trust in the unconscious.'"

Several other factors offer *permission* in Holotropic Breathwork.
For one, there is the explicit permission to express what the body
and emotions need to express. This kind of permission is hard to
find in ordinary life in our modern monoculture. For most of us,
unfortunately, the primary safe space for making loud sound is in
our cars, when we are driving alone on a freeway.

In Breathwork, trauma survivors feel *permission* to explore their
multiple dissociated pockets of experience such as: repressed
memories, emotions, sounds, movements, dissociated parts of self,
or archetypal energies.

I've told you a couple of the stories from Breathwork at the
residential recovery program. Some residents had extraordinary
breakthroughs in Holotropic Breathwork. I administered a pre- and
post-questionnaire there. At least 90% of the residents there
admitted to having experienced childhood trauma, including
childhood sexual abuse. Because I was also facilitating groups there
three times a week, in addition to Breathwork, I had an opportunity
to get to know people in a deep way, to know details about their
trauma histories, and to see whether or not Breathwork was really

helping with their trauma recovery. (See page 41 for the full presentation of this research.)

Many residents had significant reconnection to pieces of themselves, not only the traumatic pieces. One man retrieved a positive experience, which became a resource for him in dealing with his otherwise abusive childhood. He remembered his alcoholic uncles had spent time with him when he was a young child when they were sober, and he remembered that they had loved him.

In all venues of Holotropic Breathwork I facilitated, I saw some instances of severe dissociation gradually become more co-conscious as the body retold the story again and again in Holotropic Breathwork. The Breathwork experiences would retell the abuse with the same sounds, the same movements, the same needs for support over and over, with increasing awareness, change, and integration over a period of time. The set and setting of ritual provides protection, permission, and connection which allows change to be encountered—then tolerated—and finally, metabolized.

Metabolized is a wonderful word used by Mayan shaman, priest, and writer, Martín Prechtel. He talks about *metabolizing* grief. By *metabolizing*, he means the process through which we fully feel and express grief, and use our relationship to it to continue living and loving. I highly recommend his books, especially his second book, *Long Life, Honey in the Heart*, which contains heart-opening stories, that he tells as an insider, about the community and ritual culture of a Mayan village.

The difference between re-traumatization and 'metabolization' of the trauma is something added that we in Holotropic Breathwork call 'a corrective experience'.

Elements of a 'corrective experience' in Holotropic Breathwork

A corrective experience happens when a piece of trauma comes forward spontaneously through the mind, emotions, or body, and when conditions are present to allow *healing connection* instead of re-traumatization. In a corrective experience we feel safe enough to fully feel the 'un-safety of the past' and express it. When we are in a regressed state, and we can receive nurturing from another human being, that begins to correct and heal the trauma of omission. What seems to work is being held long enough and without ulterior motive, so that the defenses come down, and we can let caring and touch sink in.

Touch, sacred setting, and attention, are elements that provide a corrective experience in Holotropic Breathwork

Another element is the relative open-endedness of sessions. We allow from two to four hours for sessions. Sometimes sessions go even longer. This spaciousness of time gives permission to the inner healer to bring up whatever piece might take some time.

Trauma survivors metabolize the feelings of grief and loss by having the corrective re-experience of the trauma along with awareness, inner resources, and support. Ritual incorporates a good balance of *protection, permission,* and *connection.*

The element of *transparency*

Rituals tend to let the community see what's happening, providing the *transparency* function. There are natural ethics in small groups, tribal groups. Everything is out in the open; intimacy and safety can coexist. Holotropic Breathwork is most often done in a group setting. The group offers protection, too, as all body contact is done with permission, ethically, and in full public view of other people.

There is an additional advantage in the openness of the group. People get *permission* from watching others. They learn that they are not the only ones, and that they are not crazy if they want to express energies, movements, or sounds in Breathwork that would not be welcome in most social situations. For trauma survivors who have lived with injunctions not to know, not to tell, not to hear, and not to see, the ethical, compassionate, and witnessing group can provide a corrective experience.

More about *connection*

The participant in Holotropic Breathwork *connects* primarily with her own inner healer. As one continues to do Breathwork, that connection with the inner healer grows stronger. *Communitas* is the *connection* among equals who are bonded through their sacred experience side by side.

Another *connection* comes from the bond between the sitter and the breather. I wrote an article entitled, "The Practice of Sitting in Holotropic Breathwork." (See page 15.) It is about many of the ways the sitter/breather relationship assists in changing the internal and external relationship dynamics and patterns. The main idea is that, in each of those roles, we have a chance to experience awareness of our own inner and outer relationships.

For example, in the time-limited contract as the breather, we have the chance to put *ourselves* first and not be co-dependent or defer to what we imagine are our sitter's needs. We have a chance to express what *we* need to have somebody pay close attention to for *us*, and to have somebody act as a surrogate for our own inner witness part, while we notice a bit more about how to do witnessing for ourselves.

A breather with trauma and dissociation might be learning of her right to know what she needs, to ask for it without trying to please someone else, and to let someone else really be there for her. Parts might show up for assimilation such as the witness part, child parts, nurturing part, dissociated alters, guardians (perhaps ones called upon in childhood), or persons dead or alive from one's biography. A breather might spontaneously find a relationship growing internally between these previously repressed or dissociated parts.

Peter Levine's trauma work, as I understand it from reading his book, *Waking the Tiger,* and from talking to some who have taken his training, is partly about shuttling skillfully between emotional parts associated with the trauma and other parts that hold resources that can help contain and metabolize the grief and pain of the trauma, without letting it overwhelm the system.

Many times, the *inner healer* does most of that shuttling elegantly and internally, even automatically, in Holotropic Breathwork. Shuttling is supported, as it is happening at the end of a session, by facilitators who just *follow the process* with someone.

Sitting also has important things to teach someone recovering from trauma. I have had several regular breathers who thought less of sitting than breathing. They thought they "had to trade sitting" for the privilege of getting the real benefit, breathing. I pointed out to them that as sitters they were learning to watch their own impulses and thoughts without acting on them, and were practicing putting another part of them first by putting their breather first during the time of the session. They also had the opportunity to practice meditation with compassion and awareness of their own needy and nurturing parts at the same time they were practicing compassion and awareness for their breather.

The third stage of ritual–the *post-liminal* stage

Turner's third stage of ritual is the *post-liminal* stage in which there is integration or *aggregation* as he calls it, into a new stable state.[3] This is much like the stage when Joseph Campbell's 'Hero' returns from the 'Hero's Journey' with new understandings or gifts, which he or she incorporates into ordinary life and relationships (Campbell 1970).

The ritual adventurer in Holotropic Breathwork returns with an experience and a tangible artistic expression, such as a mandala or a SoulCollage˚ card. Then he takes the art back home, maybe, in doing so, expanding the borders of the 'village' a little bit.

Life-Crisis rituals and trauma recovery

I particularly see the tie-in between ritual and trauma recovery in the types of ritual that anthropologist Victor Turner (1967) calls *life-crisis rituals* and *rituals of affliction*.[1] The *life-crisis rituals* include rituals that mark the transition between one stage of personal development and another. Birth, puberty, marriage, and death are major examaples of such stages.

In the Ndembu tribe that Turner was writing about in 1967, *rituals of affliction* were performed for those who were "caught" by the spirits of deceased relatives whom they had forgotten or neglected. It seems to me there is an interesting parallel between afflicted Ndembu tribespeople, who were "caught by the spirits of ancestors" they had forgotten or neglected, and persons suffering from PTSD from childhood abuse. Those who had childhood abuse have often shut off, or "forgotten" the memories of these 'ancestors' as a way to deal with overwhelming pain and still survive. The tribesperson, who is the subject of a *ritual of affliction*, is "caught by the spirits of his ancestors," and the person experiencing PTSD from childhood abuse is 'caught' by his family system and its events, from which he has dissociated.

Trauma that sticks to us becomes PTSD

Trauma is not what happens to us; it is what sticks to us. I want to focus now specifically on two things: 1) trauma, particularly on why it sticks to us and becomes PTSD; and 2) what we need in the

136

way of *protection, permission,* and *connection* in order to facilitate trauma recovery.

When a traumatic event happens to us—whether it be sexual, physical, emotional, or spiritual, and whether we be child or adult or both, and if things are right, then we will have a circle of others around us. They hold us upright even when our life force wants to flee from our middle sections and leave us in a crumple. If we have community, then this community will feed us even when we are cut off from the hungry urge to feed ourselves. If we have community, there will be others who listen to us tell the same tale for as long as its gnashing, puking, images flash against our minds and bellies. If we have community, there will be others who listen to us while we forge a healing language from the fire of 'the trauma' and our own burning. If we have community, there will be others who believe us, who feel with us, and who even want to wail with us. If we have community, there will be a circle of others nodding, knowing that we are telling the truth whether we tell it concretely, or metaphorically, or show it with our faces and our bodies. And if we have community, there will be others who understand that trauma-telling, when it is intertwined with real listening and authentic empathy, synthesizes new form and strengthens life.

But, if things are out of whack, as they are in many cases of modern trauma and PTSD, we do not have these nurturing others, and we have to forget, dissociate, something, in order to survive. If we do not have the chance to call out an agony and listen to the echo of strength and beauty in our ability to sound it, we forget the wholeness of the universe and each other. If we do not have food sources in our time of need, we discount our hunger, in order to survive. If we do not have the encouragement to tell our story, we forget its force and its fierceness; we forget the betrayal, and we blame ourselves and lose ourselves, and we usually remove ourselves from the possibility of real relationship and connection.

A psychiatrist in Italy, Piero Coppo, who is also a certified facilitator of Holotropic Breathwork, once told me a story of how he had translated a psychiatric depression inventory into the language of Mali in Africa and gave the test orally to hundreds of tribespeople there. He was wondering how much depression he would find among the people there. He found zero depression.

He talked to me about the way they handle grief (and trauma recovery, it seems to me, is largely about processing grief.) He said that when a loved one died in someone's hut, several community and family people came to be near that person in his or her silent shock. Staying at a respectful distance, they were silent also. And as the days passed (as I remember him telling me) they came a little closer venturing a little more interaction. And as weeks passed, these 'sitters' (as we would call them in Holotropic Breathwork) spoke more, ventured a laugh here and there, encouraged more participation in daily activity, and, like gentle human shoe horns, slid the person back into the communal flow.

A ritual of bereavement was conducted after a month's time. A final ritual of bereavement happened between one and two years. And there was no depression among these people. Coppo wrote about this research in a 1984 article in a French journal[2] and his book *Ethnopsychiatry of Depression*, was to be published by Bollati Boringhieri, Torino in January 2005.

Hillary Clinton was right. It takes a village to raise a child. But it not only takes a village to raise a *child*, it takes a village to deal with everyone's individual grief and trauma, no matter what their age. It takes a village to ceremonially balance the relationships of humans within the larger scheme of things, with Spirit. It takes a village to remind us, as we walk around in our small stories, of the Larger Story.

Holotropic Breathwork is a modern ritual for the 'global village'

Holotropic Breathwork carries the traditional principle of 'village'. The Holotropic 'global village' is set sturdily in non-locality. One aspect of this village is the Grof Transpersonal Training, which is a gypsy caravan, holding its modules in various places, carrying its tradition along with its huge music system on its back to each new place. In this aspect of the village, people move in and out, certifying every two years or so.

Then they join the part of the global village that contains those almost 900 people who have certified, who keep in touch on a listserv, through the newsletter of the Association for Holotropic Breathwork International, and at these ITA conferences.

The global village of Holotropic Breathwork also contains the tens of thousands (maybe we're even into the 100s of 1,000s by now) of people who have participated in those one-day workshops. This global village also sets up camp as those one-day workshops, as they are happening.

The modern world has no village, no community rituals that connect families with a sense of place. We are challenged to find what is true and real, and to serve it in a new way. A true global village task is to deal deeply with the grief and trauma of the human condition. Another task is to serve Spirit and each other with compassion, without the rigidity of dogma, without the trappings of any one person's belief system held in such a way that it might keep another person from connection in his or her own way to Spirit, or to other human beings.

Holotropic Breathwork, as a modern ritual, offers one place where we can, together, metabolize grief and trauma.

The question of whether Holotropic Breathwork is 'retraumatizing'

I want to address two questions that come up a lot when we are talking about Holotropic Breathwork and trauma recovery. The questions are:

1) "Is Breathwork ever retraumatizing?" and;

2) "Are there people who shouldn't do Breathwork?"

When I was preparing this presentation, I called Tav Sparks, who is the principal trainer for the Grof Transpersonal Training, which certifies Holotropic Breathwork facilitators. I asked Tav, "Do you think there are people who shouldn't do Holotropic Breathwork?" Putting our heads together, we could remember a total of maybe 10-20 people who were not able to get much benefit from Holotropic Breathwork. That is 10-20 people in the 17 years of working with more than 1000 people who came through the GTT training. That means that only between 1% and 2% of the people who self-select to use the method of Holotropic Breathwork didn't, in our opinions as trainers, get much benefit from Holotropic Breathwork. Conversely, of course, that means 98-99% of those who self-selected to do Breathwork in the training did get benefit, again according to our collective, subjective assessment.

The 1%-2% who did not get benefit from Holotropic Breathwork is a pretty low percentage, but it is definitely an important group to which to pay attention. Tav and I talked about circumstances where, in spite of the best efforts of the facilitator to create a good environment using the Holotropic model, the person just cannot feel safe. Basically they are afraid, and they cannot differentiate inner experience from outer experience when they do Breathwork. For example, Tav says, "Some people find it impossible not to perceive the facilitator as part of the relived trauma."

140

There are a lot of possible explanations for this. One has to do with what is called 'insecure attachment', which involves a history of severe, very early trauma of omission, commission, or both. This would usually include perinatal trauma and also early infant and childhood trauma. This is really a whole topic unto itself—what prevents someone from being able to make use of Holotropic Breathwork, together with what circumstances might help someone overcome those odds to be able to make use of Breathwork.

Different levels of experience in trauma healing

I want to talk briefly also about the ability of Holotropic Breathwork to hold different levels of experience while reliving and healing from trauma.

When people relive childhoods in which they were often repeatedly intruded upon, lashed open, impaled, burned they were victims. When they were not hurt physically, but were emotionally shriveled by the hot words of parents projecting their own inadequacies, *they were victims*. At this level of personal experience, we need to hear them, to truly witness, and to tell them over and over that, "this never should have happened to you; you were an innocent child; you didn't cause this; you did nothing wrong; *it is not your fault.*"

But there is another level of experience too, and that is a level of transpersonal experience that Cynthia DeFilippo wrote about in a short article in *The Inner Door*. It was called "Healing the Sacred Wound." (1992), and we re-published it in *Exploring Holotropic Breathwork*. Some people dislike that term, 'sacred wound' if it is applied to sexual abuse. They ask, "What could be sacred about sexual abuse?" And, "What could be sacred about any trauma?"

In this article, DeFilippo described how she had breathed at our Holotropic Breathwork workshop month after month, reliving the trauma, the pain, the betrayal over and over until, in one workshop, something different happened. This is what she wrote right afterwards:

141

I fully feel the cry of a wounded animal, and also the cry of all children being raped and abused.

I feel the cry of all women in childbirth.

I feel the cry of all men at war or in prison.

I feel the cry of my father as he raped me.

I feel the cry of myself as the perpetrator raping the child and the woman.

I feel the cry of Mother Earth as we rape and kill her.

I feel no separation.[3]

Through wounding she had received personally, Cynthia had been tapped for service to her 'village'. She could see how her own agony had cracked her open to become part of others, not as a victim this time, but through her own choice, and she became grateful for her difficult path to this spiritual understanding.

This is a different level from the biographical experience; it is a transpersonal level of healing. Cynthia didn't think she could have come to this in any other way than through *the Sacred Wound* or *the Terrible Gift*, or as Ram Dass calls it, "fierce grace."

Cynthia finished her article in this way:

Once a month for two years, I entered the room where we Breathe as a group. It is like a sacred temple to me. It is a safe and nurturing place, where the parts of my life that have remained locked within are allowed 'breathing' space, recognition, and expression. The space, the music, the Breath, all encourage me to feel the un-experienced experiences. The Breath journeys me deeply into my Self, to places where my worlds split apart at a very young age.

Cynthia is describing this modern ritual of Holotropic Breathwork, and how it helped her with change, with her recovery from trauma. In between her words you can hear the elements she needed, and found in Holotropic Breathwork: *protection, permission,* and *connection.* When she writes, "Sometimes I call the room we Breathed in, "The Breathing Cathedral," you can almost feel the group *communitas.*

---

[1] Turner, V. (1967.) 94. (1968b). 576-577

[2] Coppo P. (1984.) "Syndrômes depressifs et retard mental dans une communauté rurale africaine: enquête épidémiologique", *Psychologie Médicale,* 16, 1273-1276.

[2] DeFillipo, C. (1992.) "Healing the Sacred Wound" in *The Inner Door* 4(1)3-4. Republished in Taylor, K. [Ed.] (2003.) *Exploring Holotropic Breathwork.* Santa Cruz, CA: Hanford Mead Publishers, Inc.

~9~

Jung's Fourth Function as a Gateway for Non-Ordinary States in Spiritual Emergence and Spiritual Emergency

Overview

C. G. Jung's four functions, originally identified as psychological differences in his 1921 book, *Psychological Types*, are best known today through the Myers-Briggs test and a shelf of popular books about personality types based on this test. Two of these are *Gifts Differing: Understanding Personality Type* by Isabel Briggs Myers (one of the authors of the Myers-Briggs test) and *Please Understand Me* (I and II) by David Keirsey. In addition to the four functions which are paired: intuition/sensation and thinking/feeling, the Myers-Briggs test measures the two additional pairs: judging/perceiving and extraversion/introversion and assigns an acronym for each of 16 possible combinations of these pairs. This chapter is about the connection I have noticed between the preponderance of the material occurring in a Breathwork participant's non-ordinary states of consciousness in spiritual emergence/y and, from my observations (not testing), what function the participant has as his or her fourth function. Let me first say something about spiritual emergence and spiritual emergency, and then I will discuss how they interact with the fourth function.

Spiritual Emergence

Spiritual emergence is the process by which we incorporate new knowledge from our experiences in non-ordinary states of consciousness. We then use this new knowledge to improve our way of operating in the world. *Spiritual emergence* is the term, coined by Christina Grof, which describes how we grow in understanding of the nature of ourselves, the universe, and God as we understand God. It is the common experience of expanding our sense of personal identity or our spiritual identity to include more—the experience of growing older, wiser, and more whole.

Spiritual emergence is usually a relatively slow process. Information enters the system in manageable bits in non-ordinary states (or moments) of consciousness, in flashes, in dreams, in therapy, in daydreams, in prayer, in intimate relationships, through healing touch, and in meditation. It works also in non-ordinary states of consciousness that for the most part are cordoned off from ordinary life in therapy sessions, in church services, during sleeping time, or during sex. Spiritual emergence is a term to describe a continuum of experiences that reconnect us to parts of ourselves from which we have become disconnected. In spiritual emergence, the re-connection, or new knowledge, does not impair our daily functioning, but comes and goes as there is opportunity.

When we intentionally enter non-ordinary states of consciousness in Breathwork, during prolonged prayer and meditation, in spiritual retreats, during shamanic journeys, during fasts, under hypnosis, or when participating in other deep experiential processes or therapy, we may often veer over, intentionally or not, into the fast lane. We challenge our body, mind, and spirit to integrate and expand to include rapidly acquired new information. In a spiritual emergence, we are balancing the input from non-ordinary states of consciousness with our ability to assimilate it into ordinary states of consciousness.

146

Spiritual Emergency

When does the spiritual emergence process become a spiritual emergency? A spiritual emergency or somatic-psycho-spiritual crisis is an acute episode in the course of a longer process of spiritual emergence. It happens when the process of ongoing personal development takes a rapid and dramatic course. Our ordinary functioning and control is often overrun in a spiritual emergency, unlike in a gradual emergence.

In a spiritual emergency, new awarenesses come tumbling in, one upon another. Whether the decision to answer the call of psychospiritual development is conscious or not, the same kinds of results can occur when the opening is sudden and overwhelming. We may have been seeking out philosophical answers, attending workshops, studying spiritual literature, participating in deep experiential sessions, such as Breathwork. Or we may have been surprised by an opening that seemed to move to meet us. A spiritual emergency can begin spontaneously without a conscious decision to enter non-ordinary states of consciousness for spiritual development. Even if we consider ourselves on a spiritual journey and are 'prepared' for it, we are always surprised by the form it takes and by its power.

As a river rising with unexpectedly heavy rains, new feelings, sensations, intuitions, or concepts flood over the banks of our normal control skills and beliefs, which are too small to contain them. For a period of time the flow is too rapid for us to channel. The banks, the normal control mechanisms, don't hold. We cannot utilize the new information easily because it seems to come in a form that is alien to us. Ordinary life (relationships, work, home) becomes more turbulent. The new awarenesses may seem to be in paradoxical or antithetical conflict with the old belief systems. It is a process that takes precedence in the life usually for a period of months or years, and it results in major change.

Jung's Fourth Function

Many years ago a paragraph in the wonderful little book *Knowing Woman* by Irene Claremont de Castillejo deposited in me a hypothesis that I had to test against my observations of Breathwork experience. Castillejo was writing about C. G. Jung's fourth (or inferior) function as the function which is least within our conscious control. Her brief description was my first exposure to the four functions. Geldhart (1997) describes them further:

> The *sensation* function receives physiological informa-
> tion from *real* objects. We see, hear, taste, touch, and smell
> real objects outside the body, such as apples. We *sense*
> real objects inside the body, such as muscle states and
> impulses. *Sensation* tells us that something is, but not what
> it is. The *thinking* function recognizes and tells us *what*
> that something is. The *feeling* or *valuing* function evalu-
> ates something and tells us what it is *worth* to us, and
> whether we *like* or *dislike* it. The *intuition* function per-
> ceives *possibilities* for *real, subjective,* or *intentional* ob-
> jects in a situation.[1]

Furthermore Jungian theory holds, as I said above, that the functions are paired. Intuition and sensation are linked; thinking and feeling are linked. There is a primary function which is dominant and usually skilled. The other function of each pair automatically becomes the fourth (or inferior) function in which the person is unskilled and with which he or she is unidentified. When thinking is primary, feeling is fourth. When feeling is primary, thinking is fourth. When intuition is primary, sensation is fourth. When sensation is primary, intuition is fourth.

In discussing the concept of the four functions, Castillejo identified her personal primary function as intuition and her fourth function as sensation. I recognized immediately that her pattern was the same as my own. When she wrote, "To the intuitive it is the things of the senses which are magical, not his intuitions which he takes as a

148

matter of course,"[2] I realized in one intuitive instant that the holotropic (moving toward wholeness) flow (or tidal wave) of spiritual emergency was most likely to come through the undefended doorway of whichever function was the fourth function for a given individual. I realized that many of the non-ordinary state experiences that comprise spiritual emergence and spiritual emergency enter through the doorway of Jung's fourth function. In spiritual emergency, the major difference is that the primary function may be removed from its job for a prolonged period of time, not only temporarily as during a Breathwork experience. It can be overwhelmed for a certain larger period in one's ordinary life so that one can truly explore and develop the fourth or inferior function and move towards greater wholeness.

According to Jung, one of the four functions, intuition, sensation, thinking, or feeling, would be "inferior" in each person, and would be therefore the one least developed in ordinary life and least defended against wholeness and connection to Spirit. It made sense to me that my own spiritual emergency had come through the function of sensation, the body. I had experienced the uncontrollable spasms and jerks of a kundalini type of opening. As energy moved through my body, clearing blockages during a five-year period of personal turbulence, I had felt compelled to make sounds and do automatic mantra chanting. I experienced a few physical illnesses as cleansing and catalytic. I connected to the transpersonal through the physicality of psychedelics and entheogens and through touch and sexuality. The spiritual force I 'sensed' during this time felt separate from 'me' and my ego-identified self or selves. These 'ordinary' selves were much more identified with my first three functions. I identified my self with intuition and, secondarily, with feeling and thinking. The function of sensation was, however, alien and therefore was something mysterious and compelling that I experienced as coming from 'outside of me', and even 'worshipped', with awe.

Those with sensation as the fourth function may, in ordinary states of consciousness not be particularly aware of their bodies, but in non-ordinary states of consciousness the body becomes holy, sex is felt as sacred, movement in non-ordinary states of consciousness is spontaneous and awesome. Sound is vibration. Sensation may be experienced as 'god', or it might be felt as 'demon', perhaps because body trauma is being relived and remembered and the body is being reclaimed and made whole again. Sensation may even be felt as a sense of demonic possession, because sensation itself is so alien to this type of person and to his or her ordinary experience.

If the fourth function has broken through in a spontaneous or planned non-ordinary state of consciousness, it may not be turned off easily, the dominant function may not easily find control again soon. There is something compelling, even often ecstatic, about being 'out of control' in this way and letting this function have full sway for a while, but it can also look crazy from the outside, especially if the experiential phenomena pop out in the midst of ordinary life (as happens in spiritual emergency) instead of being contained, for example, in a Breathwork session.

At the time all this was happening with my own spiritual emergency through my fourth function of sensation, I was observing my cohorts in the Grof Transpersonal Training and others who were doing Breathwork. They were not all having 'kundalini' experiences! What I have experienced, what I have seen in others, and what makes rational sense to me is that when God, Spirit, Transformation is trying to manifest through us, this holotropic[3] force takes the path of least resistance, and overall that seems to be through the fourth function, whichever one we have. The material of the divine coming through the gate of our first, second, or third functions is not recognized as divine, but when it appears at the door of the fourth, we see it as both 'other' (not of self) and as 'divine', 'mystic', and numinous.

For the person with fourth function sensation, the body is divine in non-ordinary states. For the person with fourth function intuition, psychic material and 'channeling' is divine. For the person with fourth function feeling, feelings are divine, and for the person with fourth function thinking, concepts and ideas are divine.

Some of my cohorts, for example, were overwhelmed with an influx of psychic material. The kind of spiritual emergency the Grofs have called "a psychic opening"[4] lets images, knowings, voices, and intuitions flow in from the unconscious. A person who was usually quite grounded in their primary function of sensation, who was normally concrete and adept at the details of life could be distracted for a time from ordinary activities, while trying to process, sort through, and integrate the flood of psychic information coming through his or her fourth function of intuition.

Others who were normally 'thinkers' and 'analyzers' were bowled over whenever they had a 'Feeling' with a capital 'F'. They felt a great reverence towards, or sometimes a great fear of, those feelings that had entered through their fourth function door with an intensity they had never imagined possible. A feeling was almost a god to be worshipped. "I am having a *Feeling*." Feelings were hitherto fairly unknown to these people and thus amazing, an occasion for a 'worship service'. People with fourth function feeling have been known to hold their hands in the prayer position while describing these feelings (of fear, embarrassment, sadness, etc.) quite passionately.

And then there were those whose feeling function in ordinary life was quite skilled, but the inferior function of thinking had mostly been dismissed by them as not very useful. These people felt the fourth function open in such a way that they became quite enamored of understanding systems like alchemy, the kabbalah, or astrology. Ideas were the gods, theories were fascinating, and maps held the answers. Fourth function thinking types often went back to school and got Ph.D.s. When the power of the unconscious entered through the gate of their fourth function, thinking, they became in awe of concepts and of the structures for their dissemination, such as academic institutions. Von Franz wrote: "All inferior functions have a mystical quality about them."[5]

Not being a thinking type, I didn't give the Myers Brigg's test[6] to my friends and clients to ascertain primary and inferior functions, but I 'intuited' who among us had which of the four configurations, especially when the manifestations were exaggerated by spiritual emergency. I thought I noticed too that there was a kind of death/rebirth process happening in spiritual emergency that temporarily 'killed' the primary function (or, rather, overwhelmed its attempts at control) so that the fourth function could be explored, developed, appreciated, and so that, eventually, the primary and fourth function would work together in a way that transcended the power of either separately and a new way of functioning could arise. As I would read later, Jung thought the fourth function and the primary function were allies in achieving individuation and that in each person's fourth function lay a tremendous resource—access to the power of the unconscious.

There were two times when I especially noticed the synergy of first and fourth function in my own process. A month after the kundalini process erupted for me at Esalen at a Grof monthlong workshop, I returned to work in suburban New Jersey. I was an executive director of a non-profit agency, and accustomed to doing a lot of planning, visioning, list-making (using my primary intuition and my secondary thinking functions). I found I no longer could do any of these normal intuiting and thinking activities. I couldn't plan and think ahead. I couldn't even 'daydream'. I was internally compelled to pay attention to my immediate environment, to trust my body and body/mind to be able to do what I needed to do when the time came to do it. It was a difficult learning period in which my ordinary skills were virtually taken from me, and I simply had to learn to trust and discover how to sense and observe real objects and events in real time.

I also had one strong non-ordinary session experience in which the kundalini was moving my body in rhythmic powerful ways. I was helpless to stop it as usual. I had learned by then to just relax, trust, and even appreciate it. In this particular session, at a point of greater surrender to the movement, my intuition suddenly opened again and images and understandings danced in, almost rhythmically, in time with the body movements. I felt the powerful coupling of intuition and sensation, primary and fourth function, that can occur when the two are no longer artificially separated by ego identification. From a point something like a witness, I experienced the contribution of each function and its dependence on the other. I sensed *and* intuited clearly that if my body was not moving and involved, I would not *know*.

Spiritual emergence is happening when the participant in Breathwork temporarily encourages, by breathing faster and deeper, the opening of the fourth function and the relinquishing of control by the primary function. 'Surrendering control to, trusting the inner healer' is another way to put it. In spiritual emergency the primary function takes an extended vacation, surrenders, and leaves the job of life primarily to the fourth function. Later, perhaps, there is teamwork of the primary and fourth functions and a last step may be the ability to use all four functions, as appropriate, from a place where the ego is attached to none of them. Marie-Louise von Franz wrote in her small book on *The Inferior Function*, "The sacrifice of one's first function produces a place where one neither thinks, nor feels, neither senses nor intuits. Something new comes up, namely, a completely different and new attitude toward life in which one uses all and none of the functions all the time."[7]

There is one other benefit I have found to understanding the movement of spiritual emergency through the fourth function.

Knowing that one function appears divine for oneself while another appears divine for a friend or client, really helps one honor the individuation process however it is occurring and understand someone's initial reverence for material emerging through a particular human function. At the same time it helps one laugh with a bit of cosmic humor at one's own projection that limits the divine to just one function, one's very own fourth function. With this model it is possible to see more clearly how the divine permeates each of the four functions in both our ordinary and non-ordinary experience of life.

---

[1] Geldart, W. (1997.) "The Enneagram of Consciousness and Jungian Psychology." Full Circle. Riso-Hudson Professional Enneagram Association. (3) 2.

[2] De Castillejo, I. C. (1974.) *Knowing Woman*. Harper Colophon Books. 34-35.

[3] "Holotropic" is the Grofs' term for the movement of the 'Many' toward the 'One'. "Hylotropic," on the other hand, is the complementary word for the movement of the One to take many forms.

[4] Grof, C. and S. Grof. (1990.) *The Stormy Search for the Self*. Los Angeles: Jeremy P. Tarcher. 90-95.

[5] Von Franz, M-L. (1971.) *Jung's Typology*. 39

[6] Bourguignon, E. (Ed.) (1973.)

[7] I have thought that a very interesting research project would be to correlate Myers Briggs test results with both self-reported and other-reported themes of non-ordinary states' material experienced by the subjects.

[7] Von Franz, M-L. (1971.) *Jung's Typology*. 22

Bibliography

Achterberg, J. (1985.) *Imagery in Healing: Shamanism and Modern Medicine.* Boston and London: New Science Library Shambhala.

Bache, C. M. (2000.) *Dark Night, Early Dawn: Steps to a Deep Ecology of Mind.* SUNY Press.

Boroson, M. (1998.) "Radar to the Infinite: Holotropic Breathwork and the Integral Vision," in *The Inner Door.* 10(4)5-6. Republished in Taylor, K. [Ed.] (2003.) *Exploring Holotropic Breathwork.* Santa Cruz, CA: Hanford Mead Publishers, Inc.

Bourguignon, E. (Ed.) (1973.) *Religion, Altered States of Consciousness and Social Change.*

Bradshaw, J. (1988.) *Healing the Shame that Binds You.* Deerfield Beach, FL: Health Communications, Inc.

Bragdon, E. (1988.) *A Sourcebook for Helping People in Spiritual Emergency.* Los Altos, CA: Lightening Up Press.

Browne, I. (1990, Spring.) "Psychological trauma or Unexperienced Experience." *ReVision.* (12)21-33.

Browning, R. B. (1997.) "When Darkness Brings Light." in *The Inner Door,* 9(1)4-5. Republished in Taylor, K. [Ed.] (2003.) *Exploring Holotropic Breathwork.* Santa Cruz, CA: Hanford Mead Publishers, Inc.

Bryant, D. J., J. Kessler, and L. Shirar. (1992.) *The Family Inside: Working with the Multiple.* London & NY: W.W. Norton and Company.

Campbell, J. (1970.) *The Hero with a Thousand Faces.* Cleveland: World Publishing.

Coppo P. (1984.) "Syndrômes depressifs et retard mental dans une communauté rurale africaine: enquête épidémiologique", *Psychologie Médicale.* 16. 1273-1276.

De Castillejo, I. C. (1974.) *Knowing Woman*. Harper Colophon Books.

DeFillipo, C. (1992.) "Healing the Sacred Wound" in *The Inner Door* 4(1)3-4. Republished in Taylor, K. [Ed.] (2003.) *Exploring Holotropic Breathwork*. Santa Cruz, CA: Hanford Mead Publishers, Inc.

Eckberg, M. (2000.) *Victims of Cruelty: Somatic Psychotherapy in the Treatment of Posttraumatic Stress Disorder*. Berkeley, CA: North Atlantic Books.

Frost, S. (2001.) *SoulCollage®: An Intuitive Collage Process for Individuals and Groups*. Santa Cruz, CA: Hanford Mead Publishers, Inc.

Geldart, W. (1997.) "The Enneagram of Consciousness and Jungian Psychology." *Full Circle*. Riso-Hudson Professional Enneagram Association.

Gil, E. (1990.) *United We Stand*. Walnut Creek, CA: Launch Press.

Gilligan, S. (1997.) *The Courage to Love*. NY: W.W. Norton.

Greenwell, B. (1990.) *Energies of Transformation*. Cupertino, California: Shakti River Press.

Grof, S. (2006.) *The Ultimate Journey: Consciousness and the Mystery of Death*. MAPS.

Grof, S. (2006.) *When the Impossible Happens*. Sounds True.

Grof, S. (2002.) *Psychology of the Future*. Albany, NY: State University of New York Press.

Grof, S. (1998.) *The Cosmic Game: Explorations of the Frontiers of Human Consciousness*. Albany, NY: State University of New York Press.

Grof, S. (2001.) *LSD Psychotherapy*. MAPS.

Grof, C. (1993.) *The Thirst for Wholeness*. San Francisco: HarperCollins.

Grof, C. and S. Grof. (1990.) *The Stormy Search for the Self: A Guide to Personal Growth Through Transformational Crisis*. Los Angeles: Jeremy P. Tarcher.

Grof, S. (1992.) *The Holotropic Mind: The Three Levels of Human Consciousness and How They Shape Our Lives*. San Francisco: HarperSanFrancisco.

Grof, S. (1988.) *The Adventure of Self-Discovery*. Albany, NY: State University of New York Press.

Grof, S. [Ed.] (1988.) *Human Survival and Consciousness Evolution.* Albany, NY: State University of New York Press.

Grof, S. (1985.) *Beyond the Brain.* Albany, NY: State University of New York Press.

Grof, S. (1977.) *The Human Encounter with Death.* London: Souvenir Press (Educational & Academic) Ltd.

Harner, M. (1980, 1990.) *The Way of the Shaman.* San Francisco: HarperSanFrancisco.

Hendricks, G. & Hendricks, K. (1991.) *Radiance: Breathwork, Movement and Body-Centered Psychotherapy.* Berkeley, CA: Wingbow Press.

Hocking, S. J. & Co. (1992.) *Living with Your Selves: A Survival Guide for People with Multiple Personality.* Rockville, MD: Launch Press.

Holmes, M. (1993.) "Life on the Astral Plane: A Transformational View of MPD." *The Inner Door.* Santa Cruz, California: Association for Holotropic Breathwork International. 5, 3.

Kelly, R. (1999.) "'Mask' Memories." in *The Inner Door,* 11(4)10, republished in Taylor,

Keirsey, D. (1978.) *Please Understand Me.* Prometheus.

King, S. (2001.) "Interview with Stuart Sovatsky." *The Inner Door.* 13(3)1.

Kornfield, J. (1993.) *A Path with Heart: A Guide through the Perils and Promises of Spiritual Life.* New York: Bantam.

Kripalvanand, S. (1977.) *Science of Meditation.* Bombay, India: New Karnodaya Press.

Levine, P. (1997.) *Waking the Tiger: The Innate Capacity to Transform Overwhelming Experiences.* North Atlantic Books.

Miller, Alice. (1996.) *Drama of the Gifted Child. Basic Books.*

Miller, Amy. (1993.) "Multiples Speak for Themselves." *The InnerDoor.* Santa Cruz, California: Association for Holotropic Breathwork International. 5(3). Republished in Taylor, K. [Ed.] (2003.) *Exploring Holotropic Breathwork.* Santa Cruz, CA: Hanford Mead Publishers, Inc.

Minett, G. (2005.) *Exhale.* Edinburgh: Floris Books.

Minett, G. [Ed.] (2001.) *The Spirit of Breathwork,* International Breathwork Foundation.

157

Minett, G. (1994.) *Breath and Spirit.* San Francisco, CA: Aquarian/Thorsons (Harper Collins.)

Mithoefer, M. (1997.) "The Physiology of Hyperventilation." in *The Inner Door*, 11(1)1,7-8. Republished in Taylor, K. [Ed.] (2003.) *Exploring Holotropic Breathwork.* Santa Cruz, CA: Hanford Mead Publishers, Inc.

Montagu, A. (1966.) *On Being Human.* New York: Hawthorne Books.

Muktananda, S. (1974.) *Play of Consciousness.* New York: Harper and Row.

Myers, I. B. (1995.) *Gifts Differing: Understanding Personality Type.* Davies-Black Publishing.

Orr. L. and S. Ray. (1977.) *Rebirthing in the New Age.* Millbrae, CA: Celestial Arts.

Pacey, I. (1999.) "Breathwork with Trauma Survivors: Ten Years Later" in *The Inner Door*, 11(4)1,4,9. Republished in Taylor, K. [Ed.] (2003.) *Exploring Holotropic Breathwork.* Santa Cruz, CA: Hanford Mead Publishers, Inc.

Pacey, I. (1999.) "Holotropic Breathwork, Medication, PTSD, and Depression." in *The Inner Door*, 11(1)1, 7-8. Republished in Taylor, K. [Ed.] (2003.) *Exploring Holotropic Breathwork.* Santa Cruz, CA: Hanford Mead Publishers, Inc.

Pacey, I. (1993.) "Breathwork with Trauma Survivors" in *The Inner Door*, 5(3)1,4. Republished in Taylor, K. [Ed.] (2003.) *Exploring Holotropic Breathwork.* Santa Cruz, CA: Hanford Mead Publishers, Inc.

Perry, J. W. (1989.) *The Far Side of Madness.* (Jungian Classic Series # 12.) Spring Publications.

Prechtel, M. (1999.) *Long Life, Honey in the Heart: A Story of Initiation and Eloquence from the Shores of a Mayan Lake.* Tarcher/Putnam.

Prechtel, M. (1998.) *Secrets of the Talking Jaguar: Memoirs from the Living Heart of a Mayan Village.* Tarcher/Putnam.

Riskin, T. (2000.) "Using the Model of Perintal Matrices in Psychotherapy." in *The Inner Door*, 12(3)1, 4-5. Republished in Taylor, K. [Ed.] (2003.) *Exploring Holotropic Breathwork.* Santa Cruz, CA: Hanford Mead Publishers, Inc.

Riskin, T. (1999.) "Projection and Holotropic Breathwork." in *The Inner Door*, 11(2)8-9. Republished in Taylor, K. [Ed.] (2003.) *Exploring Holotropic Breathwork*. Santa Cruz, CA: Hanford Mead Publishers, Inc.

Ross, C. A. (2006.) *The Trauma Model*. Manitou Communications, Inc

Ross, C. A. (1995.) *Satanic Ritual Abuse: Principles of Treatment*. University of Toronto Press.

Ross, C. A. (1993.) "MPD: Assessment, Diagnosis and Treatment." (Presentation at the Advanced Grof Transpersonal Training. Six audiotapes.) Boulder, CO: Sounds True.

Ross, C. A. (1989.) *Multiple Personality Disorder.* [Retitled: Dissociative Identity Disorder] New York: John Wiley and Sons.

Rothschild, B. (2000.) *The Body Remembers: The Psychophysiology of Trauma and Treatment*, W.W. Norton, Co.

Sannella, L. (1976.) *Kundalini: Psychosis or Transcendence*. San Francisco: H.S. Dakin DeVorss. Company. Republished as *The Kundalini Experience*.

Silver, J. (1999.) "Here I Sit." *The Inner Door*. Santa Cruz, CA: Association for Holotropic Breathwork International. 11(2)1. Republished in Taylor, K. [Ed.] (2003.) *Exploring Holotropic Breathwork*. Hanford Mead Publishers, Inc.

Silver, K. (1996.) "A View from the window: Considerations about Life Review and Holotropic Breathwork." *The Inner Door*. Santa Cruz, CA: Association for Holotropic Breathwork International. 8(2)1. Republished in Taylor, K. [Ed.] (2003.) *Exploring Holotropic Breathwork*. Hanford Mead Publishers, Inc.

Small, J. (1982, 1992.) *Transformers—The Artists of Self-Creation*. Marina del Rey, CA

Smith, M. (1993.) *Ritual Abuse: What It Is, Why It Happens, How to Help*. Harper SanFrancisco.

Sparks, C. (1993.) "COEX Systems and Biographical Trauma." in *The Inner Door*, 5(1)1,4. Republished in Taylor, K. [Ed.] (2003.) *Exploring Holotropic Breathwork*. Santa Cruz, CA: Hanford Mead Publishers, Inc.

Sparks, T. (1993.) *The Wide Open Door: The Twelve Steps, Spiritual Tradition & the New Psychology*. Hazelden/Hanford Mead Publishers, Inc.

Sparks, T. et. al. (1988.) "Doing, Not Doing." Grof Transpersonal Training.

Sanford, L. (1990.) *Strong at the Broken Places: Overcoming the Trauma of Childhood Abuse*. New York: Random House.

Steele, K., O. van der Hart and ERS Nijenhuis. (2001.) "Dependency in the Treatment of Complex Posttraumatic Stress Disorder and Dissociative Disorders." *Journal of Trauma and Dissociation*. 2(4), 79-116.

Tart, C. (1969, 1972.) *Altered States of Consciousness*. Anchor Books/John Wiley & Sons.

Taylor, K. (2007.) *The Holotropic Breathwork Facilitator's Manual*. Santa Cruz, CA: Hanford Mead Publishers, Inc.

Taylor, K. (2004.) "Self-Relations in Holotropic States of Consciousness: Articulating the Therapeutic Relationship in Holotropic Breathwork™" in Gilligan, S. [Ed.] (2004.) *Walking in Two Worlds*. Zeig, Tucker & Theisen.

Taylor, K. [Ed.] (2003.) *Exploring Holotropic Breathwork: A Decade of Articles from* The Inner Door. Santa Cruz, CA: Hanford Mead Publishers, Inc.

Taylor, K. (1996.) "Sitting with Life, Sitting with Death." *The Inner Door*. Santa Cruz, CA: Association for Holotropic Breathwork International. 8(4)2. Republished in Taylor, K. [Ed.] (2003.) *Exploring Holotropic Breathwork*. Hanford Mead Publishers, Inc.

Taylor, K. (1995.) *The Ethics of Caring: Honoring the Web of Life in Our Professional Healing Relationships*. Santa Cruz, CA: Hanford Mead Publishers, Inc.

Taylor, K. (1994.) *The Breathwork Experience: Exploration of Healing in Non-Ordinary States of Consciousness*, Hanford Mead, CA.

Taylor, K. (1991). "On Being Seen, Heard, and Touched." *The Inner Door*. Santa Cruz, CA: The Association for Holotropic Breathwork International. 3(2) 5. Republished in Taylor, K. [Ed.] (2003.) *Exploring Holotropic Breathwork*. Hanford Mead Publishers, Inc.

Terr, L. (1992.) *Too Scared to Cry*. New York: Basic Books.

Turner, V. (1967.) *The Forest of Symbols: Aspects of Ndembu Ritual*. Cornell University.

Van der Kolk, B. et. al [Ed.] (1996.) *Traumatic Stress: The Effects of Overwhelming Experience on Mind, Body, and Society*. Ingram Books.

Von Franz, M-L. (1971.) *Lectures on Jung's Typology*. Continuum International Publishing Group

Weil, A. (1978.) *The Natural Mind*. Mariner Books.

Index

Other Books by Kylea Taylor

The Ethics of Caring: Honoring the Web of Life in Our Professional Caring Relationships by **Kylea Taylor**. As a textbook, for supervision, or as a personal

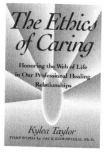

resource, this book provides unique help to professional caregivers (therapists, massage practitioners, ministers, hospice staff, etc.) It helps the caregiver sort out transference and countertransference occurring with spiritual and transpersonal issues that intermingle with the more well-known ethical issues of money, sex, and power. This is one of the few books that addresses the ethical challenges in doing spiritual or transpersonal healing work. Foreword by author, **Jack Kornfield**.

The Breathwork Experience: Exploration and Healing in Nonordinary States of Consciousness by **Kylea Taylor**. A clear, concise, and complete description of breathwork using examples from actual breathwork experiences in participants' own words. Discusses the transpersonal and perinatal theories of Stanislav Grof, M.D. and the opportunities in breathwork for healing trauma and assisting recovery from addiction. Also available in Italian: *L'esperienza della Respirazione Olotropica.*

Exploring Holotropic Breathwork: Selected Articles from a Decade of *The Inner Door*. Edited by **Kylea Taylor**. This book collects 144 field reports, published from 1991-2002, about Holotropic Breathwork and non-ordinary states of consciousness. These 85 authors, trained by Stanislav Grof, M.D., originally wrote from 15 different countries to share professional experience and theory with their peers. Covers many topics related to healing in non-ordinary states of consciousness. Hardcover, 604 pages.

Hanford Mead Pubishers, Inc.
www.hanfordmead.com

The Holotropic Breathwork Facilitator's Manual by Kylea Taylor. This Manual is *only available for sale to those who are enrolled in or have completed the Grof Transpersonal Training* (see www.holotropic.com for information and purchase.) Content includes information relevant to Holotropic Breathwork including: ethics, bodywork, trauma recovery, music, challenging situations, and how to prepare for and facilitate a Holotropic Breathwork workshop. A comprehensive index provides easy reference to the contents and other resources. The Manual comes with a Library CD which includes customizable forms and outlines.

Other Books
from Hanford Mead Publishers

The Wide Open Door: The Twelve Steps, Spiritual Tradition & the New Psychology by Tav Sparks This book connects The Twelve Steps of Alcoholics Anonymous to some of the world's greatest spiritual philosophies. The book invites us to rediscover the Source behind the Steps through direct personal experience within ourselves and with our Higher Power and discusses the experiences of surrender, death and rebirth, and wholeness, especially in doing Eleventh Step work.

Through Thunder: An Epic Poem of Death and Rebirth by Tav Sparks In the midst of his stormy years and dark night of the soul, twenty years ago, Tav Sparks spontaneously wrote this "epic" poem, *Through Thunder*. *Through Thunder* feels and sounds us through the archetypal "Hero's Journey" described by Joseph Campbell. It draws the perennial, turbulent, death-rebirth map of psychospiritual awakening, a process experienced by the mystics of all religions.

Hanford Mead Pubishers, Inc.
www.hanfordmead.com

Damanhur: The Story of the Extraordinary Italian Artistic and Spiritual Community by **Jeff Merrifield**. This is the story of the Federation of Damanhur, a 30-year-old community that has achieved 'impossible' tasks and carved the Temples of Humankind, an "eighth wonder of the world" into a mountain in northern Italy. People who are working on the forefront of change in diverse fields (science, art, music, education, healing, bio-sustainability, ecology, and spirituality) will be interested in this community's extraordinary accomplishments. Damanhur is a place where dreams are realized, where ideas beyond reason are given a chance, and where, very often, these visions become reality. This book is the story of how and why this can happen. Eight color plates and 150 black and white photographs.

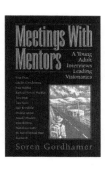

Meetings with Mentors: A Young Adult Interviews Leading Visionaries by **Soren Gordhamer**. This twenty-something author interviews **Ram Dass, Jack Kornfield, Joan Halifax, Sam Keen, Ondrea Levine, Arnold Mindell, John Robbins,** and six other teachers and authors, asking them to give tell their personal stories as guidance for young people. He asks them about mentorship, rites of passage, right livelihood, social action, and how young people can live in a way that is inwardly rich and outwardly responsible. Their responses engage, entertain, and reveal how to find one's own unique contribution in life.

Hanford Mead Pubishers, Inc.
www.hanfordmead.com

SoulCollage®
from Hanford Mead Publishers

SoulCollage®: An Intuitive Collage Process for Individuals and Groups by Seena B. Frost. *Today's Librarian* called this book an "exciting, spiritual 'craft' book for making personalized Tarot-like cards." Unlike Tarot, Soulcollage® cards are personal, made with images people select intuitively from magazines and photos. Simple directions enable anyone to create a beautiful deck of cards that has deep personal meaning. SoulCollage is a satisfying artistic way to inner exporation, and to encourage identification and expression of inner feelings in educational, spiritual, or therapeutic group settings. It is fun, too. More than 200 examples of cards are included in the book.

SoulCollage® Card Pack - These 12 blank cards make it easy to begin creating one's own personal SoulCollage deck. Instructions in the book help you use the language of symbols, dreams, and archetypes, collage them into your deck, and answer life's questions with your own inner wisdom. Made of quality matboard, these blank cards are professionally cut to 5 x 8 inches.

Introduction to SoulCollage® CD by Seena B. Frost. The author of "SoulCollage™" provides encouragement to use one's own sense of inner direction and gives practical information for using SoulCollage to connect more to self, others, and Spirit. Frost also leads a guided relaxation through the chakras.

Facilitating SoulCollage® in Groups CD by Seena B. Frost. Frost shares her decade of experience facilitating SoulCollage® in groups, talks about the "*I Am One Who...*" exercise, and gives many supportive suggestions.

See www.soulcollage.com for more information about SoulCollage®.

Hanford Mead Pubishers, Inc.
www.hanfordmead.com